the Forth Naturalist and Historian

Volume 13

Forth Naturalist and Historian, volume 13

Published by the Forth Naturalist and Historian Editorial Board,
The University, Stirling, 1990.

The Board is a University/Central Regional Council collaboration.

ISSN 0309-7560

ISBN 0 9514147 4 7

Supported by BP in Scotland

Cover Loch Katrine from Murray and Pullar's 1901 *Bathymetric Survey of the Scottish Lochs*

Printed by Meigle Printers Ltd., Tweedbank Industrial Estate, Galashiels.
Set in Palacio on Fyne White Silk Paper.

ANNUAL CLIMATOLOGICAL BULLETIN NO. 11, 1989

S. J. Harrison
University of Stirling

THE WEATHER OF 1989

Temperature and rainfall values referred to in the following are taken from Stirling Parkhead unless otherwise stated.

The weather provided us with a very eventful 1989. The year started with exceptionally high daytime temperatures more than 4.0°C above the average. There was virtually no snow on lower lying ground and daffodils began to bloom as early as February 2nd in Bridge of Allan. This was also the year of floods and gales; the railway bridge in Inverness collapsed during floods on February 7th. In contrast, May, June and July were exceptionally warm and dry and there was talk of water shortages in some parts of Scotland by the end of July. Fog was more frequent than usual for the Stirling area but air frosts were rare until December. Global warming continued to be one of the most newsworthy weather items (See Note 1).

January. Very mild and damp.

As an anticyclone drifted eastwards into continental Europe on the 1st and 2nd the wind freshened south-westerly and cloud cover was continuous. Fronts moved eastwards across Scotland from the 3rd but pressure remained generally high and rainfall amounts were small. Pressure increased from the south-west on the 6th bringing low cloud and some drizzle for the next few days. The minimum temperature fell to only 9.2°C early on the 8th (10.1°C at Bridge of Allan). As a deep depression moved towards Iceland on the 10th the wind freshened to reach gale force by the 11th which was an exceptionally wild day. After a brief respite on the 12th another deep depression to the south of Iceland brought storm force south-westerly winds on the 13th and 14th with driving rain. The wind remained very strong until the 16th after which pressure began to increase from the south and the weather became fine but cool. Fronts produced rain again on the 20th after which the sky cleared under a weak ridge of high pressure, bringing fog and the only frost of the month on the 23rd. As pressure fell from the west the weather became unsettled again on the 24th with rain in a freshening south-westerly wind. Pressure rose rapidly on the 28th and the last days of the month were mild and dull.

February. Mild but rather windy.

While pressure remained high to the south of the British Isles Scotland was brought into a run of fresh to strong south-westerly winds. Rain fell as a series of fronts crossed quickly eastwards. As small waves developed along a slow moving frontal system over north-west Scotland on the 6th and 7th this area received very heavy and continuous rain, which resulted in severe flooding and the eventual collapse of a railway bridge in Inverness. In stark contrast, to the south of the frontal system, the weather was dry and bright in Stirling. In clear spells night temperatures fell sharply but frosts occurred only at ground level on the 8th. The weather remained unsettled with rain in a fresh to strong wind which reached gale force between the 13th and 15th. There was local structural damage in the Stirling area on the 13th. In the wake of a cold front on the 15th the temperature fell in a fresh north-westerly breeze which brought blustery snow showers. As skies cleared under a ridge of high pressure on the 16th, night temperature fell to −2.6°C but rose again as further Atlantic systems arrived on the 17th. By the 19th, Scotland was in a cold polar airstream and in the much lower temperatures rain began to turn to sleet and snow. From the 19th the weather remained cold and as low pressure became slow moving over the North Sea after the 26th minimum temperatures fell to the lowest of the winter in a cold northerly arctic airstream.

March. Mild and very wet.

Daytime temperatures were remarkably consistent for the first 25 days. A series of frontal troughs dominated the weather for the first week but rainfall amounts were generally very small. A ridge of high pressure extended north-eastwards on the 7th which resulted in an overnight frost, but unsettled weather returned on a wet 8th and lasted until the 15th and 16th which were sunny. As pressure increased from the west the westerly breeze died away and the 17th was calm but cold (minimum −3.6°C). However, the high pressure soon yielded to yet more active Atlantic systems from the 18th onwards and the next seven days were wet and, at times, blustery. Rain turned to sleet and occasional snow between the 20th and 23rd. A vigorous depression to the north of Scotland brought strong westerly winds and driving rain on the 23rd and 24th. The weather quietened down a little after the 25th as a ridge of high pressure moved in from the west and Easter Monday (27th) was warm (13.7°C, 15.1°C at Bridge of Allan). As the ridge crossed the British Isles on the 28th it gave one fine sunny day before rain returned on the 29th.

April. Cold and mainly dry.

A ridge of high pressure extended south-westwards from Scandinavia on the 1st which brought the first spell of cold easterly winds in 1989. The air was relatively dry but a dusting of snow fell on the 3rd. A shallow and complex area of low pressure drifted north-westwards over the British Isles from the 5th in which the weather was cold and grey. More vigorous lows and associated fronts cleared the air on the 8th and more unsettled weather persisted until the 12th when pressure gradients became slack and the wind dropped almost to calm. Cloud amounts were variable for the next few days with some pleasantly sunny interludes and cold nights. A ridge of high pressure extended southwards across Britain on the 17th and the weather remained sunny and bright until the 21st when a series of weak fronts began to drift slowly southwards bringing some rain which turned to hail then snow by the 23rd. Snow showers continued to fall in a cold NNW airstream until the 27th when pressure began to increase from the south-west bringing Scotland into a mild westerly airstream with cloud and rain.

May. Warm and dry.

With high pressure over south-east England, an exceptionally mild south-westerly airstream affected Scotland in which night temperatures fell to only 10.2°C on the 4th (11.0°C at Bridge of Allan). Rain fell in weak frontal troughs but amounts were small. As the high became more firmly established over Britain the skies cleared on the 3rd and the following four days were sunny and very warm, reaching 21.1°C at Bridge of Allan on the 7th. Pressure began to fall slowly from the 8th and cloud amounts increased in a freshening WSW breeze. A weak low moved south-eastwards from Iceland on the 10th to be centred over the Hebrides on the 11th which was a damp day. Rain persisted into the 12th as the low drifted slowly eastwards. A deep depression became slow moving to the south-west of Ireland on the 13th which resulted in unsettled but very mild weather until the 19th when an anticyclone became established to the east of Scotland. Winds were light south-easterly to calm and the 19th to 23rd were hot and sunny. By the 23rd, however, the weather had become oppressive and thunderstorms were widespread in England bringing flooding to many areas. Although pressure remained high, weak fronts kept skies cloudy until the 26th after which the weather became fresher. As the high drifted eastwards the wind veered to a showery and cool north-westerly.

June. Very warm mid-month and quite dry.

An anticyclone remained stationary to the west of the British Isles for the first week but a series of shallow depressions and troughs resulted in unsettled weather with occasional rain. By the 8th the high had given way to a complex cyclonic system, the wind backed south-westerly and daytime temperatures rose slightly. High pressure extended north-eastwards across Britain after the 13th and the weather became sunny and, at times, very hot over the following week, reaching 28.8°C on the 19th (31.8°C at Bridge of Allan). Was this the beginnings of a real summer at last?! As the high drifted westwards from the 20th, temperatures fell slowly in a cool north-westerly breeze. In the wake of a cold front on the 23rd, daytime maximum temperatures fell below 20°C after a run of eleven glorious days. A series of complex lows and associated troughs moved in to replace the high pressure on the 24th and the weather became unsettled, cool and wet for the remainder of the month.

July. Exceptionally warm and dry.

High pressure became established over Britain by the evening of the 1st and was to dominate the weather until the 25th. An anticyclone moved very slowly north-eastwards across Scotland for the first five days, which were sunny and very warm. A thundery low moved northwards out of France on the 5th bringing severe storms to the southern half of England for several days but central Scotland remained dry until the 8th when the rain reached us from the south. With high pressure to the west of the British Isles the 10th and 11th were unsettled in a fresh WNW airstream but by the 12th the skies had cleared again and the following days were sunny and very warm with occasional haar. The anticyclone having crossed the British Isles began to decay and by the 20th had been replaced by a complex non-frontal cyclonic system in which visibility was poor in low cloud, drizzle and fog. Temperatures, however, remained high, particularly at night (minimum 14.7°C on the 22nd). The low had filled by the 23rd which brought a return to very hot but unpleasantly humid weather. High pressure retreated southwards from the 24th and the 25th to 29th were unsettled with occasional rain in a fresh westerly breeze. The wind veered north-westerly on the 30th bringing two fresh days to end the month.

August, Mild and very wet.

With high pressure to the south-west of Ireland the first four days were bright in a fresh north-westerly breeze. A shallow depression and associated fronts drifted slowly eastwards across Scotland on the 4th and continuous rain was falling by the 5th. As the depression filled, it was replaced by a succession of complex cyclonic systems maintaining unsettled weather for the remainder of the month. Winds were fresh to strong south-westerly on the 14th and 20th as deep depressions tracked to the north of Scotland. Thunder was heard on the 15th and 19th.

The 48hr rainfall total on the 19th/20th was 26.9mm (33.2mm at Bridge of Allan); the 24hr fall on the 30th was 21.2mm (18.2mm Bridge of Allan).

September. Dry, warm at times.

Pressure was high at the beginning of the month but weak fronts brought long cloudy periods with some brighter spells over the first two weeks. A weak warm front lying across northern England on the 7th brought continuous drizzle. The easterly winds turned round to the west on the 13th heralding ten days of less settled weather as a series of vigorous fronts crossed Scotland. Heavy overnight rain on the 19th/20th was accompanied by gale force southerly winds. As pressure began to increase from the south on the 23rd the weather entered a more settled interlude and the 24th was the warmest day of the month (20.3°C). While the rest of Britain remained dry, a weak front lingered over Scotland on the 25th giving intermittent light rain. Visibility improved on the 26th in the wake of a cold front and the period up to the 30th was generally calm with heavy dewfall.

October. Mild damp and windy.

No sign this month of any autumn frosts. An anticyclone to the north-west of Ireland moved slowly eastwards across Scotland over the first four days. Mornings were damp with poor visibility, usually clearing to sunny intervals before noon, although it remained dull all day on the 3rd. Atlantic systems followed in behind the high and continuous rain fell on the 5th. The weather remained a little unsettled for the next eight days although amounts of rainfall were small and there were some brighter days. A large anticyclone pushed steadily eastwards into England and continental Europe from the 14th and as the sky cleared briefly, air temperatures fell almost to freezing (0.5°C at Bridge of Allan on the 15th). The high limited itself to southern England so Scotland was brought into a westerly airstream which occasionally reached gale force and in which rainfall was intermittently heavy. By the 19th most of Britain was affected by strong winds and rain as a series of deep depressions tracked between Iceland and northern Scotland. After a brief respite on the 26th under a transient ridge of high pressure, two very deep depressions dominated the weather for the remainder of the month. Driving rain in an easterly gale overnight on the 27th/28th brought the greatest 24hr fall for the month (13.3mm; 17.6mm at Bridge of Allan).

November. Wet at first, becoming dry and cold.

High pressure lay to the south-west of Britain for the first five days bringing Scotland into a cool polar airstream and a freshening westerly wind. Rainfall was showery and total falls were slight. As a shallow low lingered off north-east Scotland on the 5th temperatures fell as the clouds cleared. By the morning of the 6th the air temperature had fallen to below freezing (−2.2°C) for the first autumn frost. The westerly wind freshened again on the 9th and fronts moved in from the west bringing more rain. By the 13th high pressure had begun to extend westwards from continental Europe which dominated the weather until the 17th. Days were occasionally bright in a cool south-easterly breeze. A complex low developed to the west of Britain on the 17th and deepened as it moved to become stationary off Cape Finisterre. Continuous light rain fell all day on the 18th. While the low persisted, Britain experienced a cold easterly airflow but night temperatures remained well above freezing under an 8/8 cloud cover. High pressure began to extend south-eastwards from Iceland on the 21st and the skies began to clear. As a result, night temperatures fell very quickly to below freezing, reaching −6.0°C on the 27th. A weak front returned the cloud cover early on the 28th which lifted night temperatures. The 29th and 30th were cloudy and dull.

December. Cold and generally dry.

High pressure extending westwards from continental Europe dominated the weather for the first eleven days. An anticyclonic gloom descended for three days with dense fog. The fog didn't clear until late on the 3rd resulting in a sharp fall in overnight temperature to −4.8°C. Fog and cloud returned on the evening of the 5th and persisted until the 11th when clearing skies brought a return to night frosts. Shallow lows developed along a frontal trough bringing a fall in pressure from 1024mb on the 10th to 990mb on the 15th, but while the southern half of Britain experienced torrential rain and floods, central Scotland received only isolated outbreaks of snow in a freshening easterly wind. There were blizzards in the Lothians on the 14th which brought chaos to Edinburgh but snowfall in the Stirling area was generally light. Temperatures were, however, low with night cooling to below −4.0°C on the 14th, 15th and 16th at Bridge of Allan. A deep depression approached south-west Ireland on the 16th bringing not only a sharp rise in temperature but also strong winds and continuous moderate to heavy rain and sleet with isolated thundery outbreaks. The 43.8mm falling in 24 hours (48.8mm Bridge of Allan) on the 16th made it the wettest day of 1989. As the depression crossed central Scotland on the 17th the pressure fell to below 950mb in the morning. As it rose again in the afternoon the wind freshened WNW. Severe storm and flood damage occurred throughout England and Wales. A ridge of high pressure allowed night temperatures to fall below freezing on the 18th/19th but as an occluded front moved slowly northwards across Scotland on the 20th temperatures rose quickly in a steady drizzle. This turned to snow at only modest elevations and some local main roads became passable only with care. Fronts passed north-eastwards across Scotland on the 23rd and 24th bringing a 48hr rainfall of 26.5mm (31.9mm Bridge of Allan) in a fresh south-westerly wind. The weather brightened up for Christmas Day and Boxing Day as high pressure began to extend southwestwards from Scandinavia. However, freezing fog formed on the 27th and didn't clear over two very cold and raw days. The high began to retreat slowly eastwards after the 29th and a warm front which was almost stationary across western Ireland brought a little rain late on the 31st There were a remarkable 18 airfrosts (20 at Bridge of Allan) during December, and 80% of the month's rain fell on just two days.

DATA SOURCES

1 Stirling (Parkhead)

Grid Reference: NS 815 969 – University gardens. Elev. 35m. Aspect: South-east. Shelter Index: 33.2 (Slightly sheltered). Established 1970. Monthly returns of daily observations are submitted to the Meteorological Office. During 1989 there were some incorrect values and gaps in the observations. Where possible these have been estimated by cross-reference to nearby Bridge of Allan. Weekly observations of ground-level rainfall continued to be made.

2 Ochil Hills (Carim)

Grid Reference: NN 864 049 — upper catchment of the Burn of Ogilvie near to the ruined Carim Lodge. Surrounded by open moorland. Elev. 332m. Aspect: North-west. Shelter Index: 16.6 (Exposed). Established: 1980. An autographic recording station serviced on Mondays. Very few days' data were lost during 1989. The tipping bucket raingauge was replaced by a tilting syphon gauge with a weekly chart. Monthly totals have been derived from weekly rainfall totals. Sub-division of weekly totals overlapping between months has been derived on a proportional basis using Stirling (Parkhead). The replacement Automatic Weather Station was installed in the latter half of the year.

3 Bridge of Allan (Westerlea)

Grid Reference: NS 795 964 — Suburban back-garden station. Local shelter from trees and houses, otherwise open aspect across the Carse of Stirling (Forth Valley). Elev. 10m. Aspect: South-east. Shelter Index: 46.5 (Sheltered). Established: 1984. Non-standard equipment and exposure. Six's Max-Min thermometer on a north-facing post at 1.8m above ground level. Calibrated regularly. Home-made plastic raingauge conforming as far as possible to standard. Stevenson's screen and standard thermometers to be installed during 1990.

CLIMATOLOGICAL AVERAGES

Climatological averages are usually calculated for periods of 30 years (temperature) or 35 years (rainfall). This is because in Britain there is an inbuilt year to year variation in all the parameters which we use to define climate. Averages based on a smaller number of years may be unduly biased by one extreme value. As there are only 19 years of records for Stirling (Parkhead) and nine for Ochil Hills (Carim) the averages published in Tables 7 and 8 should be used with caution.

Index tables pp 14-19

NOTES

1 Global Warming

The news media have grabbed this as being one of the most newsworthy weather stories of the year. Tropical storms and drowning Pacific island communities, to melting polar ice-sheets and disappearing ski-runs, all appeared with great frequency in the columns of the national newspapers and in TV and radio special reports. A seminar was held at 'No. 10' and Mrs Thatcher made announcements in New York, so clearly the global warming problem is generating some high-level political heat. The Climatic Hazards Unit here in Stirling has been asked to produce reports on possible impacts, has appeared on TV and radio, and has been widely quoted in the press. The question still remains, however, as to whether we are any more confident that the current warm and windy winters are anything more than a natural fluctuation. The convergence of many scientific predictions and the persistence of global weather patterns that appear to be in accord with them has added not inconsiderable weight to the case for accepting global warming as a real problem facing humanity.

What can not be deduced from the current predictions is how global warming will affect Scotland. When we look at the weather in central Scotland over the last nineteen years the evidence for progressive change is far from conclusive. There does appear to have been a progressive increase in annual rainfall totals which has been traced back to the 1950's in western Scotland although 1989 seems to have been an exception to such a trend. However, an analysis of mean air temperatures is considerably less conclusive (see Figure 1). Annual mean temperatures for Stirling (Parkhead) show little change except perhaps for the vaguest suggestion of a *decrease* since the warm mid-1970's, with only the last two years being remarkably warm. Summers (J, J, A) appear to be following more of a cyclical pattern of change roughly every eight years. Winter (D, J, F) mean temperatures show a general *downwards* trend since the early 1970's with only the most recent winters reversing this. Whether we can draw any conclusions from such analyses is doubtful without corroboration from other sites but it places in perspective the more outrageous of claims that *everywhere* is experiencing long-term increases in mean temperature. The fact is that global warming will result in very complex changes which at any one location won't necessarily conform to any simple long-term trend. Although the global-scale models predict certain broad changes for mid-latitude maritime locations, the complex interaction of weather patterns, sea-surface temperatures, and topography make it almost impossible to be certain what will happen in Scotland over the next few decades.

2 Summer 1989

Over much of the British Isles summer 1989 was one of the sunniest this century, the warmest since 1983, and the second driest since 1727 (driest was 1959). (Source: Met Office *Outlook* Winter 1989). However, in human terms, the drought was nowhere near as severe as 1976 and water restrictions were more of a threat than a reality in many places. In Scotland, the 'summer' came to an abrupt end in a soggy August. Daily maximum temperatures weren't the highest on record but the exceptional persistence of hot days inflated the mean temperatures well above normal.

3 Effects of Elevation

During 1989 the average difference in daily maximum air temperature between Stirling (Parkhead) and Ochil Hills (Carim) stations was 4.6°C which is equivalent to a lapse-rate of 15.5°C per 1000m which, like 1988, is exceptionally steep and reflects, in part, the contrast in exposure between the two stations. In contrast, the average difference in minimum temperature was only 0.8°C or a lapse-rate of 2.7°C per 1000m. The difference in mean temperature was, as in 1988, 2.7°C, a lapse-rate of 9.1°C per 1000m.

Further to the work on freeze-thaw frequencies which we published during 1988, an analysis has been carried out of the frequency of 'inversions' of daily minimum temperature between the same stations (Inversion = upper station warmer than the lower). There is a clear seasonal pattern of highest frequency in autumn and lowest in spring.

Over the last 6 years there has been a steady increase in the frequency of inversions in autumn (Figure 1B) resulting from an apparent increase in frequency of anticyclonic weather patterns.

The difference in annual precipitation between the two stations during 1989 was 593mm giving a gradient of change of 2.00mm m^{-1} (*cf* 1981-89 average 1.76mm m^{-1}).

4 Climatic Hazards Unit (CHU)

Most of the research being undertaken by the Unit is now reported in its Annual Report and will no longer appear in the Annual Climatological Bulletin. This year has seen the conclusion of the British Rail contract, the continued development of the Severn Estuary Aerial Inputs Programme and the start of negotiations with the Met Office to place collaboration on a formal contractual footing. A number of smaller contract jobs have been undertaken which have helped to establish the Unit as an important centre for research into weather/climate impacts on society in Scotland. A recent innovation has been the introduction of training courses in basic meteorology which have been directed principally at road engineers. At the time of writing the Unit is in the process of installing equipment for receiving Meteosat images in addition to an automatic weather monitoring system.

5 In-Service Workshops for Geography Teachers

These highly successful workshops have continued to be offered during 1989. The most recent customers have been independent schools in Scotland and northern England (September 1989) and schools in Strathclyde Region (January and February 1990). Further workshops are planned – for details please contact Dr Harrison in the Department of Environmental Science. The background notes from the workshops are to be published in the next issue of the Scottish Association of Geography Teachers Journal. Ideas for the analysis of routine weather data from a single station are available free of charge from Dr Harrison.

6 Register of Weather Stations

Since the last Bulletin there has been some support for a fully revised edition of the Register. Discussions have been held with a commercial sponsor and the use of available database technology is being explored.

7 Weather Data for Schools

With the increase in demand from schools for basic weather data and advice on a range of weather events there is an urgent need to improve the channels of communication between suppliers and consumers. It is clear that with the arrival of the investigation element in the Standard

Grade Geography syllabus it will be impossible to operate on the basis of responses to enquiries from individuals. Stirling's Climatic Hazard Unit has already experienced great difficulty dealing with the 40 Highers project enquiries it received during 1988/89. The Met Office centres in Glasgow and Edinburgh are already similarly stretched. Some of the pressure has already been relieved through the use of information packs but even these will not be able to stem the flood of potential demand in the years ahead. As a first step towards developing an efficient means of making weather information available in schools there was a one-day seminar at the University of Stirling early in May 1990 attended by representatives of the Met Office, Royal Meteorological Society, Climatic Hazards Unit and others, and to which regional subject advisers, or their representatives, were invited. For more details contact Dr Harrison.

8 Reference Material

The Microclimatology Laboratory (4B125) in the Cottrell Building of the University contains an increasing amount of reference material, including climatic data (local, national and global), synoptic weather data and scientific reports. The CHU was recently given a run of the Quarterly Journal of the Royal Meteorological Society by R. W. Gloyne, a well-known agro-meteorologist. Monthly summaries of observations from Stirling (Parkhead) and Ochil Hills (Carim) are currently being transferred from VAXA to the new Hewlett Packard system and will be available for general access in due course. (Contact Dr Harrison for file specifications).

Use of these data in publications should be acknowledged.

9 Publications

Harrison, S. J. Long-term impact on global geography in D. J. Pullinger Scorching Heat and Drought: A Report on the Green-House Effect. St Andrews Press p23-30.

Harrison, S. J. and Smith, K. (*Eds*). Weather Sensitivity and Services in Scotland. Scottish Academic Press 180 pp.

Rowling, P. Rainfall variation and some implications for flooding in the Allan catchment, central Scotland. *Weather* 44(4), 146-154.

N.B. Single copies of the Annual Climatological Bulletin are available to schools free of charge. Further copies cost £1 each and are obtainable from the Department of Environmental Science, Stirling University.

	Mean Maximum °C	Difference from Average	Highest Maximum	Lowest Maximum	Mean Minimum °C	Difference from Average	Highest Minimum	Lowest Minimum	Mean °C	No. days No. of <0°C	Mean Soil Temp. °C (0.3m at 09)
January	10·3	+4·3	12·0	5·8	4·1	+3·9	9·2	−0·4	7·2	1	6·2
February	10·5	+4·1	12·2	6·9	1·6	+1·1	8·6	−4·2	6·1	9	5·3
March	10·6	+2·0	13·7	8·4	1·5	0	7·1	−3·6	6·0	7	4·9
April	11·4	−0·2	13·6	8·8	2·5	−0·6	6·9	−2·9	6·9	7	7·6
May	18·1	+3·1	23·2	11·5	6·1	+0·6	10·5	0·5	12·1	0	12·3
June	19·0	+1·5	28·8	13·3	8·8	+0·5	15·7	0·8	13·9	0	14·9
July	22·5	+2·7	27·5	15·6	10·4	−0·3	14·7	5·3	16·5	0	17·1
August	19·0	0	23·1	15·6	10·3	+0·4	16·0	2·1	14·7	0	16·3
September	16·6	+0·6	20·3	12·6	8·6	+0·4	14·5	0·5	12·6	0	14·1
October	15·0	+2·2	19·2	10·7	4·1	−1·3	9·9	0·3	9·5	0	11·2
November	10·2	+1·3	14·6	4·4	1·8	−0·6	6·4	−6·0	6·0	8	6·8
December	6·9	−0·2	10·5	2·1	−0·9	−2·3	4·5	−5·0	3·0	18	2·7
YEAR	14·2	+1·8	28·8	2·1	4·9	+0·1	16·0	−6·0	9·5	50	10·0

Table 1 Monthly Temperatures (Stirling, Parkhead) 1989

	Mean Maximum °C	Difference from Average	Highest Maximum	Lowest Maximum	Mean Minimum °C	Difference from Average	Highest Minimum	Lowest Minimum	Mean °C	Difference Parkhead to Carim	No. days < 0°C
January	6·3	+3·5	9·6	2·5	2·8	+3·7	6·3	– 1·0	4·5	2·7	3
February	4·6	+2·0	8·0	0·0	0·5	+1·9	5·4	– 4·2	2·6	3·5	11
March	5·4	+0·5	9·8	0·1	1·0	+0·9	6·8	+3·5	3·2	2·8	9
April	6·1	−2·0	10·1	1·0	0.6	−0·7	5·0	– 5·1	3·3	3·6	10
May	12·2	+0·7	19·1	6·3	5·0	+0·8	11·8	−0·1	8·6	3·5	2
June	14·1	+0·2	24·5	7·8	6·6	−0·3	13·0	−1·1	10·3	3·6	1
July	18·8	+2·5	24·6	12·3	9.6	+0·5	14·3	3·9	14·3	2·2	0
August	15·5	0	19·3	12·2	9·4	+0·5	13·9	3·3	12·3	2·4	0
September	12·8	+0·5	16·0	9·8	7·0	−0·1	11·5	0·2	9·9	2·7	0
October	10·6	+1·4	13·6	6·5	5·2	+0·4	9·0	2·2	7·9	1·6	0
November	5·4	−0·5	10·0	2·1	2·0	+0·2	5·5	– 3·4	3·7	2·3	5
December	3·3	−1·0	7·6	−0.7	−0·6	−1·1	3·3	−6·0	1·4	1·6	17
YEAR	9.6	+0·7	24·6	– 0·7	4.1	+0.6	14·3	– 6·0	6·8	2·7	58

Table 2 Monthly Temperatures (Ochil Hills, Carim) 1989

Stirling / Carim

	Stirling: Total Precipitation	Percentage of Average	Percent of Accum. Average	Greatest fall in 24 hours		Number of Days				Carim: Total Precipitation	Percentage of Average	Percent of Accum Average
				Amount mm	Date	Precip. Recorded	0·2mm or more	1·0mm or more	5·0mm or more			
January	98.0	95.9	95.9	19.2	13th	19	17	17	6	168.9	108.5	108.5
February	111·1	192·5	130·8	17·6	25th	23	21	19	8	(187.5)	208.3	145.1
March	134.0	159.9	140.8	19.8	9th	23	23	20	9	210.4	124.9	136.9
April	26.6	65·4	130·0	4·3	30th	15	15	11	0	65.4	96.5	131.2
May	26·8	43·9	114·8	9·6	11th	11	8	5	2	33.4	32.7	114.0
June	47·5	90·1	111·5	9·1	12th	14	12	8	3	68.7	95.5	112.0
July	18·6	29·9	100·5	6·4	25th	8	7	5	1	68.5	81.0	108.4
August	110·5	152·8	107·6	21·0	30th	23	21	15	8	201.6	149.4	114.7
September	71·5	74·7	102·6	16·5	19th	12	12	10	7	91.8	58.1	106.1
October	84·3	90·0	101·0	13·3	27th	21	21	17	6	168.2	96.6	104.7
November	33·0	32·2	92·4	8·7	10th	12	12	7	2	46.6	36.6	98.2
December	79·6	81·6	91·2	43·8	16th	10	10	9	3	124.3	70.1	94.9
Year	841·5	91·2	–	43·8	16/12	191	179	143	55	1435.3	94.9	–

Table 3. Monthly Precipitation (Stirling: Parkhead) 1989

Table 4. Monthly Precipitation (Ochil Hills, Carim) 1989 (Based on Weekly Totals)

	Mean Maximum °C	Highest Maximum	Lowest Maximum	Mean Minimum °C	Highest Minimum	Lowest Minimum	Mean °C	Precipitation mm	Greatest Fall in 24 hours	
									Amount mm	Date
January	9.9	12.8	6.6	4.3	10.1	−2.0	7.1	114.1	27.2	11th
February	9.2	13.0	2.8	1.6	8.7	−6.0	5.4	104.5	26.2	24th
March	10.6	15.1	7.0	1.8	7.2	−3.8	6.2	141.3	21.5	9th
April	11.7	17.0	6.3	1.9	6.0	−3.7	6.8	28.9	7.6	11th
May	18.1	26.1	9.2	6.4	11.1	−0.1	12.3	24.4	7.9	24th
June	20.4	31.8	13.4	8.4	16.0	−0.3	14.4	51.2	8.1	13th
July	24.6	30.0	18.9	10.9	15.0	4.4	17.7	17.3	5.8	25th
August	19.5	24.1	13.1	10.5	15.9	3.0	15.0	116.3	21.7	19th
September	17.4	21.8	14.0	8.1	13.8	1.6	12.7	77.9	16.0	19th
October	15.3	19.6	11.5	6.8	14.0	0.5	11.0	88.9	17.6	27th
November	9.0	15.5	−0.5	2.0	7.6	−6.3	5.5	36.5	9.1	10th
December	5.3	11.0	0.1	−1.4	5.6	−6.7	2.0	93.0	48.8	16th
YEAR	14.3	31.8	−0.5	5.1	16.0	−6.7	9.7	894.3	48.8	16/12

Table 5 Temperature and precipitation data for Bridge of Allan (Westerlea Drive) 1989

	NUMBER OF DAYS								
	Air Frost	Precipitation				Snow Lying at 0900	Snow Fall 09-09	Fog at 0900	Thunder Heard 09-09
		Recorded	0.2mm or more	1.0mm or more	5.0mm or more				
January	3	20	19	17	6	0	0	1	0
February	5	23	23	18	8	6	6	0	0
March	6	25	23	20	9	2	5	0	1
April	9	14	13	11	1	1	3	0	0
May	1	9	8	5	2	0	0	0	0
June	1	13	11	9	5	0	0	0	0
July	0	8	8	5	1	0	0	3	0
August	0	24	20	17	8	0	0	0	2
September	0	16	13	10	5	0	0	4	0
October	0	23	22	15	5	0	0	2	1
November	9	15	12	8	3	0	0	2	0
December	20	14	13	10	3	2	1	9	1
YEAR	54	204	185	145	56	11	15	21	5

Table 6 Weather frequencies for Bridge of Allan (Westerlea Drive) 1989

	Maximum Temperature °C	Minimum Temperature °C	Soil Temperature (0.3m at 09.00) °C	Total Precipitation mm
January	6.0	0.2	2.9	102.2
February	6.4	0.5	2.7	57.7
March	8.6	1.5	4.3	83.8
April	11.6	3.1	7.5	40.7
May	15.0	5.5	11.5	61.0
June	17.5	8.3	14.7	52.7
July	19.8	10.7	16.6	62.2
August	19.0	9.9	16.2	72.3
September	16.0	8.2	13.7	95.7
October	12.8	5.4	10.2	93.7
November	8.9	2.4	6.2	102.6
December	7.1	1.4	3.8	97.6
YEAR	12.4	4.8	9.2	922.2

Table 7 Climatological Averages for Stirling (Parkhead) 1971-1989

	Maximum Temperature	Minimum Temperature	Total Precipitation mm
January	2.8	−0.9	155.6
February	2.6	−1.4	90.0
March	4.9	0.1	168.5
April	8.1	1.3	67.8
May	11.5	4.2	102.1
June	13.9	6.9	71.9
July	16.3	9.1	84.6
August	15.5	8.9	134.9
September	12.3	7.1	157.9
October	9.2	4.8	174.2
November	5.9	1.8	127.3
December	4.3	0.5	177.2
YEAR	8.9	3.5	1512.0

Table 8 Climatological Averages for Ochil Hills (Carim) 1981-89

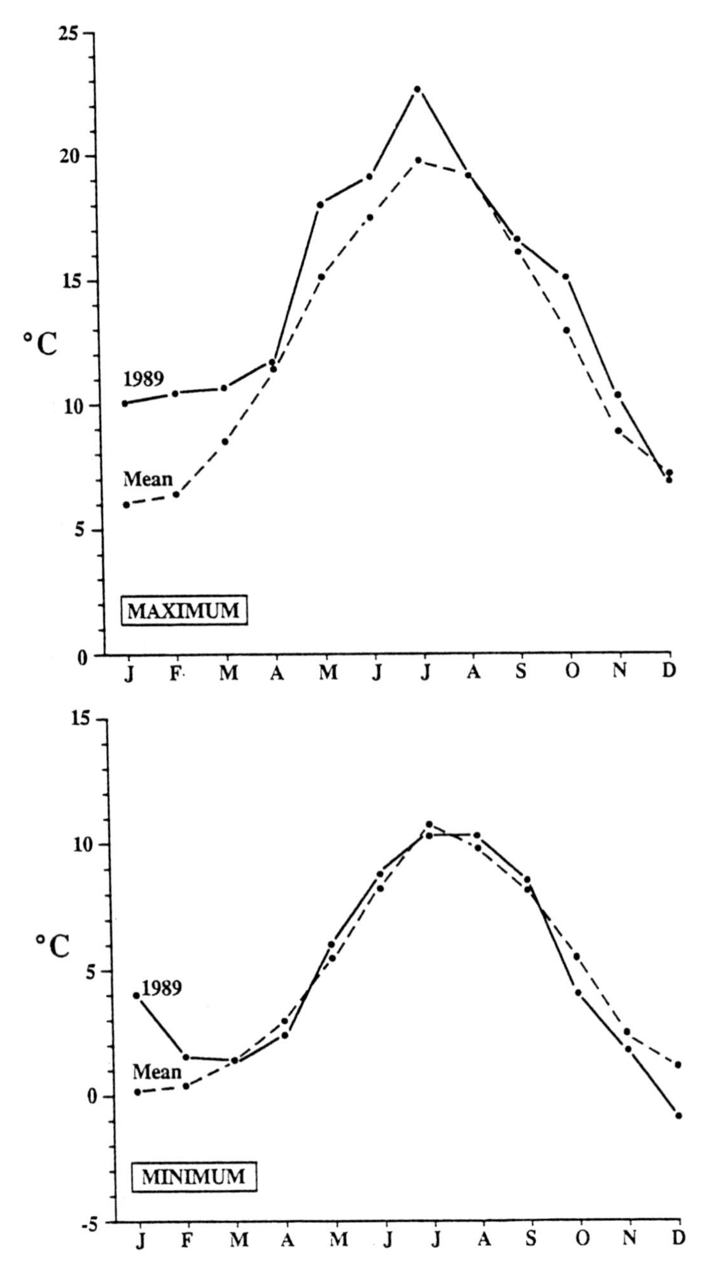

Figure 1 Monthly air temperature (max, min, mean) at Stirling (Parkhead) 1989

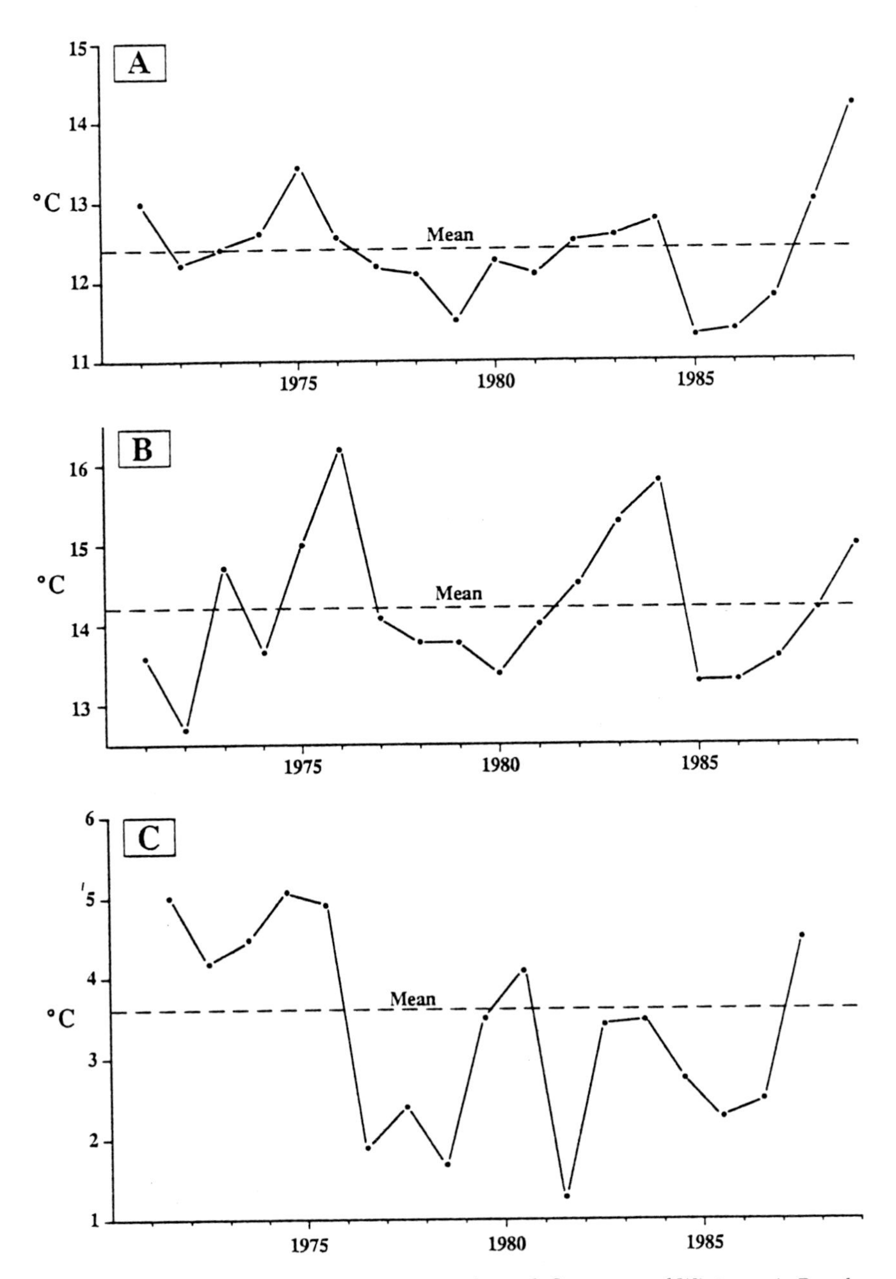

Figure 1A Changes in air temperature, Annual, Summer and Winter – A, B and C, at Stirling (Parkhead) 1971-1989.

Figure 1B Variation in frequency of temperature inversions (min. temp.) between Stirling (Parkhead) and Ochil Hills (Carim) in autumn months (Sept., Oct., Nov.) 1983-9

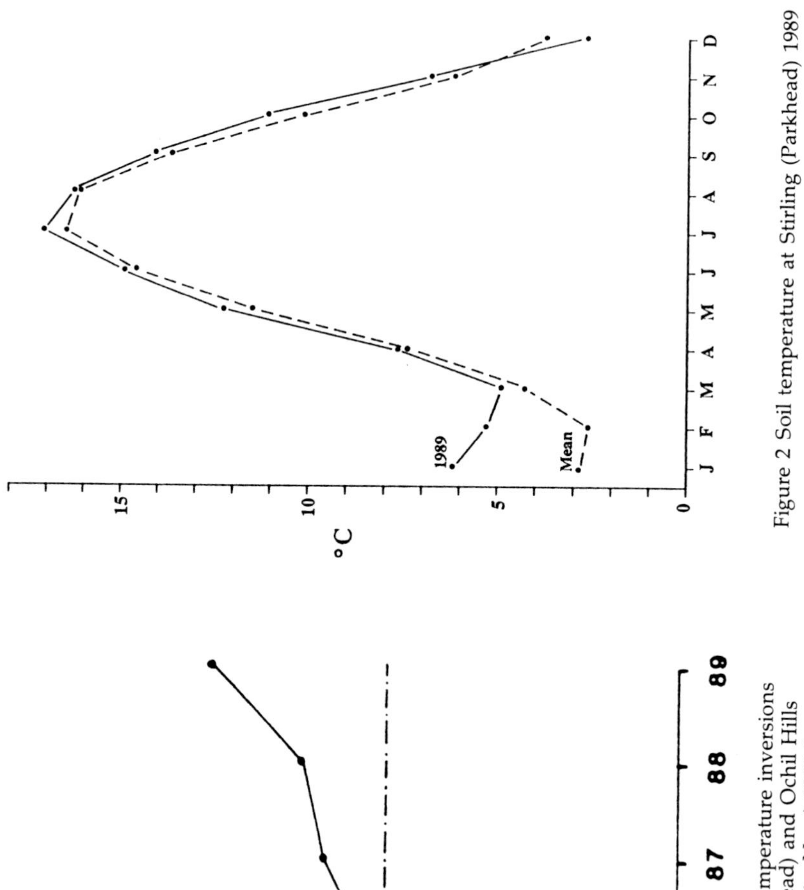

Figure 2 Soil temperature at Stirling (Parkhead) 1989

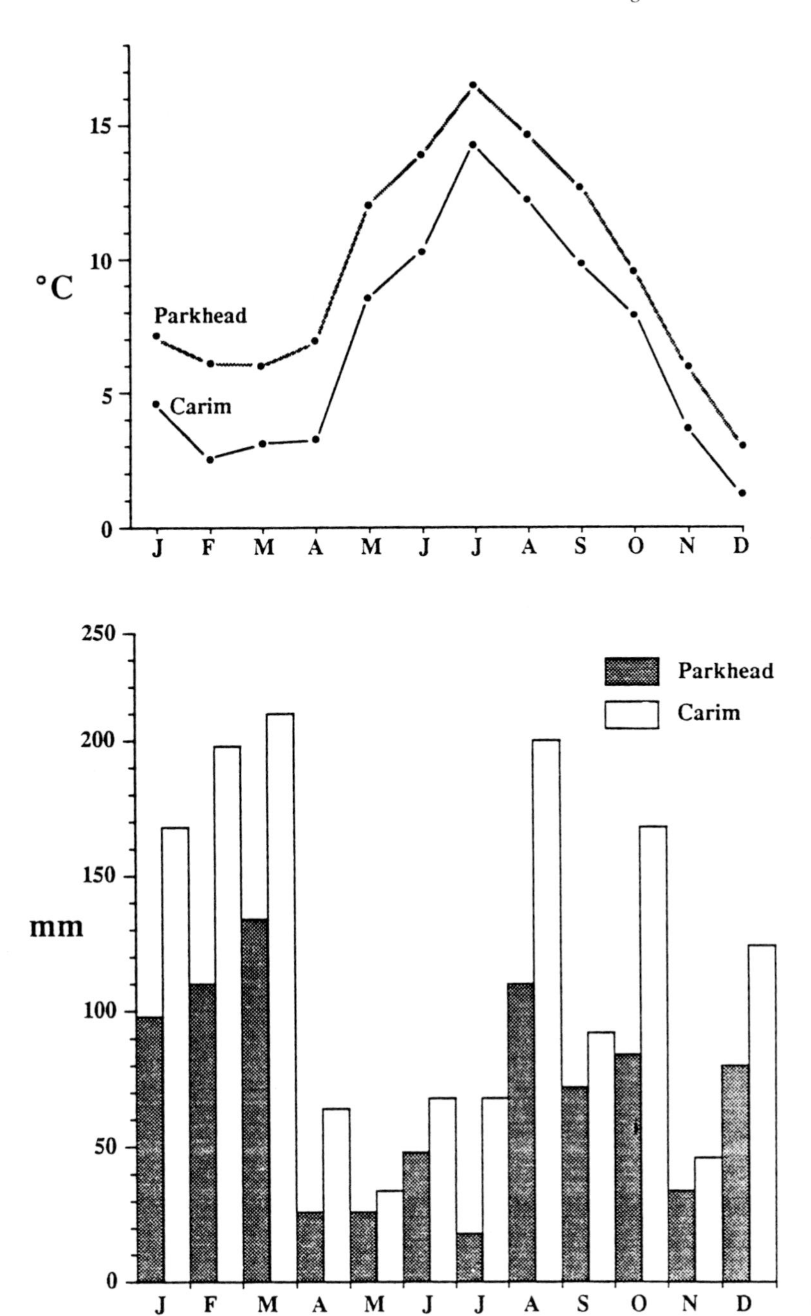

Figure 3 Temperature and precipitation comparisons between Stirling (Parkhead) and Ochil Hills (Carim) 1989.

EDITORIAL NOTES

In hand for volume 114 are: Enclosures — a Farmer's View by Lewis Stewart; Rock Art of Menteith by Maarten Van Hoek, and by Lorna Main; Excavations at Airth by Geoffrey Bailey. Expected are: Climate Report 1990, and Global Warming by J. S. Harrison; Birds of the Devon by Cliff Henty; Communion Services in Georgian Stirling by Andrew Muirhead; and a People of the Forth essay on Smith of the Museum.

Two possible new books in progress are: *The Economy of Alloa in its Days of Prosperity* by J. Milne — the 1830s to early 1900s; *The Lure of Loch Lomond* by R. MacAlasdair — a descriptive tour of the loch and its islands.

If we achieve some basic sponsorship we hope to produce *Central Scotland* a new survey of the area to succeed *The Stirling Region* produced in 1974 by the University for the British Association. An intent is to produce this in 1992, the 25th anniversary of the University.

The Ochil Hills booklet has been further delayed but Spring 1991 is hoped for — this and a revised *Mines and Minerals of the Ochils* are joint ventures with the Clackmannanshire Field Studies Society.

A History of Doune and Kilmadock Parish has been proposed by Jayne Stephenson and Callum Brown in the next three or four years.

The Young Forth Environmentalist Awards are to continue in 1991 — prizes expectantly by the Bank of Scotland.

Suggestions for a theme for the 17th *Man and the Landscape* symposium for November 1991 will be welcomed, as will offers of papers, studies, 'People of the Forth' essays for possible publication.

Commissioning of 1890s maps from Alan Godfrey is continuing — recent ones have been Doune and Callander, Dunblane East and West, Denny and Dunipace. Larbert/Stenhousemuir is in press, and Balfron is planned.

Another joint lecture with Airthrey Gardens Group is under consideration on the subject of George Forrester or the Scottish Plant Hunters.

THE CHARTING OF SCOTLAND'S LOCHS

R. W. Duck
University of St. Andrews

The innumerable lochs and lochans of Scotland are, arguably, the most significant scenic legacy of the Pleistocene glaciation. They vary from tiny col or corrie-lochans to long, deep basins occupying large valleys and have resulted principally from ice scouring of valley floors or from damming by glacial deposits. A glance at almost any Ordnance Survey map of Scotland, especially one covering highland terrain, instantly reveals the large numbers and varieties of sizes and shapes of lochs present. In addition, most are depicted with bathymetric contours giving the depths of water in the basins. It is easy to take a great deal for granted when studying an Ordnance Survey map. Not only is the immense work which went into the original topographic surveying easily forgotten, but the task of finding out the depths of the water bodies is probably seldom, if ever, given no more than a passing thought. Yet a fascinating story, with a strong connection to the Stirling area, lies in the work behind these 'mere lines' drawn on the lochs on a map.

In the pre-metric days of the One Inch to One Mile Ordnance Survey maps each bore the legend, "Contours in lochs are given in feed and are taken from the Bathymetrical Survey of Fresh Water Lochs of Scotland". On today's 1:50,000 scale series maps the bathymetric contours are converted into metric intervals and no reference is made to the original source of information thus creating a further element of mystery. So, what of these surveys of the lochs; when were they carried out, by whom, how and why?

The story begins in the early 1880s. The key figure at this stage was John Murray (later Sir John Murray), the distinguished oceanographer. Canadian-born of Scottish parents, Murray had played an important role in the famous cruise of the *Challenger* from 1872 to 1876. Following this and subsequent deep sea expeditions, in which he was involved in the exploration of the physical and biological conditions of the great ocean basins, Murray returned to Scotland where he had studied at Edinburgh University. His intention was to carry out nearshore oceanographic investigations around Scotland. To this end, with the financial assistance of his good friend Mr Laurence Pullar of Bridge of Allan, Murray built the 30 ton steam yacht *Medusa*. From the year 1848 until 1891 she was engaged in the exploration of the shallow waters and deep sea lochs around the country. During this work Murray became acutely aware that almost nothing was known about the depths of the freshwater lochs. In the interests of navigation, naval officers had surveyed Lochs Awe and Lomond around 1860 and Murray himself had made a few depth soundings along the centre lines of the lochs connected by the Caledonian

Canal. However, this represented the total knowledge of the depths of Scotland's fresh-water lochs at that time.

In consequence Murray proposed a systematic survey of all the Scottish freshwater lochs which would, he wrote, "in all likelihood result in many new additions to natural knowledge, and would be especially important for comparison with results in other departments of scientific endeavour" (Murray 1910). Murray understood that geologists were especially keen to learn the depths of loch basins in connection with discussions as to their modes of formation. Fishermen and water supply engineers were also interested in this subject. Hence on Murray's initiation the proposal was brought before the Councils of the Royal Societies of Edinburgh and London. Both Councils endorsed Murray's plans and, during 1883 and 1884, strongly urged the government of the day under Gladstone to support such work "in the interest of scientific progress". Disappointingly, but today one may cynically say not surprisingly, these representations failed to achieve the backing of the government. They were unable to sanction the proposal since such a survey fell under the remit of neither the Admiralty, whose work was confined to the interest of navigation, nor the Ordnance Survey, whose operations were limited to *terra firma*.

Murray was not content to let his idea die and was determined that a survey of the freshwater lochs be carried out. However, his scheme appears to have lain dormant for several years until it was revitalised by the keen support of Frederick Pattison Pullar, son of Murray's friend Laurence, and together they agreed to undertake the work at their mutual expense. In the absence of proper financial support, they initially regarded the project as a "holiday task" and it was not until 1897 that their surveys commenced.

In the meantime J. S. Grant Wilson, an officer of the Geological Survey of Scotland, had carried out soundings in the 'chief Perthshire lochs', namely Lochs Tay, Rannoch, Earn and Tummel, in connection with his studies of the glaciation of that district. For these water bodies he recorded maximum depths of 510, 420, 268 and 124 feet, respectively. The results of this pioneering work including small, coloured bathymetric maps were published in the Scottish Geographical Magazine (Grant Wilson, 1888). Little is known of Grant Wilson's methods or the equipment he used save that he took a series of depth soundings, 50 to 80 yards apart (presumably with some kind of weighted line), along parallel traverses, from one side of a loch to the other, spaced at intervals of about a quarter of a mile. The observations were checked by other soundings taken on lines extending along the lengths of the lochs. A steam launch was employed on Loch Tay, while for the other lochs a rowing boat proved adequate.

Murray and Pullar chose to begin their formidable undertaking with the lochs in the drainage basin of the River Forth, in particular those of the Trossachs and Callander area. By 1990 they had published bathymetric maps of Lochs Katrine, Arklet, Achray, Vennacher, Drunkie, Lubnaig, Voil and Doine in the Scottish Geographical Magazine (Murray and Pullar 1900). A year later charts of the remaining lochs of the Forth basin, Chon, Ard, Leven and the Lake of Monteith, together with two of the Tay basin, Ericht and Garry, appeared in the same journal (Murray and Pullar 1901a,b).

Before commencing their work proper, the two surveyors had made many trial attempts to measure water depths using various devices. As none had proved entirely satisfactory, Pullar, who was a highly inventive man, designed and built what was to become known as the F. P. Pullar Sounding Machine. This was mounted on the gunwhale of a boat and comprised a drum wound with galvanised steel wire which passed around a measuring pulley to a tubular weight. The system was such that for every one foot of wire which ran out, the measuring pulley made one complete turn. The motion of the pulley was transmitted to a series of dials which indicated the length, in feet, of line paid out in the water. This ingenious piece of apparatus was so successful and reliable that it was employed in all surveys except those in small, poorly-accessible hill lochs where graduated hand lines were used (Murray 1910).

With only 15 charts completed between 1897 and the beginning of 1901 the target of surveying all of Scotland's lochs must have seemed virtually impossible to Murray and Pullar. Then in February 1901 tragedy struck. On the 15th of that month Pullar lost his life at the age of 25. He drowned whilst heroically attempting to rescue a number of skaters who had fallen through thin ice into Airthrey Loch, near to his home at Bridge of Allan. Murray, who had been out of the country for some months on a round the world voyage, arrived back in Britain in time to learn of his young friend's death the previous day (Chumley 1901; Murray 1910).

This disaster brought the loch survey work to a halt. Indeed Murray wrote that it was his intention to abandon it altogether. However, convinced as to the scientific merit of the project, Pullar's father Laurence wished that the work should continue as a memorial to his son. To expediate this he set £10,000 in trust as the means for carrying on the surveys and took Frederick's place as co-director.

Now placed on a secure financial footing, the work was resumed in the spring of 1902. The level of funding enabled the employment of a team of scientific and technical staff on the project. Indeed 48 personnel took part, for longer or shorter periods, as well as numerous boatmen and assistants employed temporarily in different parts of the country. By 1909, when the field operation was drawn to a close, an enormous total of 562 Scottish lochs had been surveyed. ''All lochs were surveyed'', wrote Murray, ''on which boats could be found at the time the work was being carried out''. This impressive total was made up not only of the 'well known' major lochs but also numerous smaller and less familiar sites throughout the country, including many in the Shetland, Orkney and Western Isles. In all the surveyors took over 60,000 soundings of water depth.

When measuring water depth it is vital that the position of the boat is accurately established. The loch surveys were conducted along traverses between known end points, often buildings or prominent shoreline features such as deltas at the mouths of burns. Uniform spacing of soundings was achieved by recording the depth after a fixed number of strokes by the oarsman. In order to maintain position when running lines of soundings, an aligning mirror was often used on the boat. In this way an object onshore behind the surveyor could be kept in line with another feature in front.

While the surveys were in progress, other studies of water temperature, movements and chemistry, loch biology, the nature of the bottom deposits and the geology of the sites were also carried out. The bathymetric charts, masterpieces of cartography, were prepared and colour-printed by Dr J. G. Bartholemew of Edinburgh at a scale of 3 inches to 1 mile. The soundings were contoured at regular intervals, each division being coloured in a shade of blue becoming progressively darker with water depth. The charts, together with a descriptive account of each loch, chapters on the associated scientific work and numerous tables of statistics relating to the lochs, were collated into six volumes and published by the Challenger Office, Edinburgh (Murray and Pullar 1910). The price for this record of a truly remarkable scientific endeavour was 5 guineas.

The deepest sounding measured in all 562 surveys was of 1017 feet in Loch Morar. The second deepest loch was found to be Loch Ness (maximum 754 feet) followed by Loch Lomond (632 feet), Loch Lochy (531 feet), Loch Ericht (512 feet), Loch Tay (508 feet), Loch Katrine (495 feet) and Loch Rannoch (440 feet). In his introduction to the six volumes Murray reflected that, "It was rather amusing at times to observe the result of the soundings on the inhabitants of districts in which the lochs are situated. As a rule, lochs, or some parts of a loch, are regarded as very deep or without bottom. When a loch with this reputation was found to be relatively shallow, the result would be questioned, and a feeling of affront or injury prevailed among the inhabitants of the district".

Since the days of Murray and Pullar the face of the Highlands has changed considerably. The advent of hydro-electric power generation has seen the construction of large numbers of concrete dams. these have created many new artificial lochs such as Loch Faskally and Loch Errochty. In other sites dams have raised the water levels, and thereby the surface areas, of pre-existing natural lochs, as for example in the case of Loch Tummel and Loch Garry. Natural changes have also occurred in the lochs, principally associated with the ever-continuing building forward of cones of delta deposits at the mouths of influent rivers and burns. But what of the deposition of fine grained sediment particles on the bottoms of the lochs at hidden depths? In other words, how fast are the lochs filling up with grains of silt and clay carried in by streams? To answer this question repeaty surveys are required for comparison with those of Murray and Pullar.

In recent years a number of resurveys (very few when compared with 562) have been attempted on various loch around the country. These include several of the major Tay and Forth basin lochs, notably Lochs Earn, Tay, Tummel and Lubnaig (Al-Ansari and McManus 1980; Duck and McManus 1985; Duck 1986). Not surprisingly the techniques of surveying used today have changed considerably (McManus 1982). The electronic echo-sounder, which records water depth continuously whilst a boat is in motion, replaces the sounding line, the outboard motor supersedes oar propulsion and radio position fixing enables the location of a boat to be known to within about two metres. The time taken to complete a survey has thus greatly decreased as it is no longer necessary for the boat to be held stationary during sounding.

In general terms the major lochs which have been re-examined are infilling with sediment at very low rates, of the order of 1 to 2mm per year. Locally, however, sediment deposition is sometimes more significant. But perhaps the most striking and important feature to emerge from the new surveys is just how good the old ones were. Despite the very considerable advances in surveying techniques the bathymetric contours determined today are, almost without exception, directly comparable with those plotted by Murray and Pullar. The old surveyors, with what now seem very primitive methods, missed very little indeed.

No group of scientists are ever likely to come near to repeating the great work which Murray and Pullar directed. Their bathymetric surveys, together with all the associated researches, must go down in history as one of the most ambitious and monumental pieces of natural scientific work ever accomplished. Even eighty years on, few countries can boast such comprehensive exploration of their freshwater lakes. Moreover, the work of Murray and Pullar deserves wider recognition that it enjoys today.

REFERENCES

AL-ANSARI, N. A. and McMANUS, J. 1980. A reinvestigation of the bathymetry of Loch Earn. *Scottish Geographical Magazine* 96, 105-113.

CHUMLEY, J. 1901. The late F. P. Pullar. *Scottish Geographical Magazine* 17, 148-150.

DUCK, R. W. 1986. Bottom sediments of Loch Tummel, Scotland. *Sedimentary Geology* 47, 293-315.

DUCK, R. W. and McMANUS, J. 1985. Bathymetric charts of ten Scottish lochs. *Tay Estuary Research Centre Report* No. 9, University of Dundee, 31 pp.

GRANT WILSON, J. S. 1888. A bathymetrical survey of the chief Perthshire lochs and their relation to the glaciation of that district. *Scottish Geographical Magazine* 4, 251-258.

McMANUS, J. 1982. Scottish lochs: physical and sedimentological investigations. *Forth Naturalist and Historian* 7, 22-29.

MURRAY, Sir J. 1910. The fresh-water lochs of Scotland. Introduction. *In* Murray, Sir J. and Pullar L., Bathymetrical Survey of the Scottish Freshwater Lochs 1, 1-28, Challenger Office, Edinburgh.

MURRAY, Sir J. and PULLAR, F. P. 1900. A bathymetrical survey of the fresh-water lochs of Scotland. Part I The lochs of the Trossachs and Callander district. *Scottish Geographical Magazine* 16, 193-235.

MURRAY, Sir J. and PULLAR, F. P. 1901a. A bathymetrical survey of the fresh-water lochs of Scotland. Part II The remaining lochs of the Forth basin. *Scottish Geographical Magazine* 17, 113-128.

MURRAY, Sir J. and PULLAR, F. P. 1901b. A bathymetrical survey of the fresh-water lochs of Scotland. Part III The lochs of the Tay basin. *Scottish Geographical Magazine* 17, 169-175.

MURRAY, Sir J. and PULLAR, L. 1910. Bathymetrical survey of the Scottish Freshwater Lochs. Challanger Office, Edinburgh, 6 volumes.

BOOK REVIEW

The Battle of Bannockburn: a Study in Mediæval Warfare. W. M. Mackenzie. Strong Oak Press, Stevenage. 1989. 124 pp. Hbk. ISBN 1 871048 03 6. £8.95.

An attractive reproduction of the author's intensively researched analysis of **the** battle of Scottish history, its causes and related events. First published in 1913 it differed radically from the then generally accepted accounts, and claimed to be based on studies of the poem *The Bruce* and other 14th century literature. He published his edition of the poem in 1909 and the basis of this book in the 1910 *Transactions of the Glasgow Archaeological Society*.

It is compulsive reading. Its five chapters covering the general strategy of the war, the armies and movements, details of the main phases of the battle on 23 and 24 June 1314, and the varied interpretations in later history. Mackenzie remarks on the effect on the English of the sight of the shouting, banner and stick-waving 'little people' – servants, civilians . . . . This was reputedly led by a young Kinross, later rewarded with land in Stirling, probably that of the locally famous Kinross coachworks. A George Kinross was a notable Provost in the 1880's, and we have a wing of over 100 student flats at Stirling University which mark the generosity of a more recent member of the family, the business tycoon, House of Fraser man, John Blythe Kinross, CBE, 1904-1989.

L. Corbett

CENTRAL REGION BIRD REPORT 1989

C. J. Henty
University of Stirling

This report, like all previous ones, is based on information submitted to the author as one of the regional Bird Recorders in the scheme set up by the Scottish Ornithologist's Club. Our own area is the Central Region excluding Loch Lomondside. We overlap with Clyde Branch in publishing records for Carron Valley Reservoir and in the first instance these should be sent to the Clyde Recorder.

The year started with a very mild winter and an influx of Waxwings, though there is no reason to imagine any connection. High numbers of Whooper Swans and Pinkfooted Geese were on the Stirling carse until the middle of spring though flocks of Greylag Geese continue to be relatively small. Kingfishers are being reported more widely, no doubt due to a succession of mild winters, but there is so far little sign of any recovery of Stonechats. Corn Buntings are hanging on only in farmland by the Forth in the southeast of the region but Yellow Wagtails seem to have finally vanished as a breeding species. We just managed to participate in the 1989 influx of Quail.

The fine summer weather assisted field work on the second year of the national survey of breeding birds and some examples of results from my own 10km square are included. At the time of writing (August 1990) the final season of this project has ended, all the squares in our area have received basic coverage but the intensity of survey work varies a lot and hence the total list of species for some squares is clearly incomplete. It is hoped to include some more information from this survey in the next report.

Records are particulaly wanted from the high mountain areas and from the coast from between Bo'ness and Blackness; also all information on species that are easily overlooked such as the owls and Woodcock. Finally, a cautionary tale on the need to make descriptions of unusual birds: a small bird that flew one November night into a Stirling bistro was photographed next day before release, unfortunately the photograph was a disaster and hence the suspicion that this unlikely encounter was with the first Firecrest for the region must remain purely a suspicion.

Contributors to 1989 Report–

C. E. Barth, W. E. Brackenridge, R. A. Broad, M. V. Bell, E. Blake, D. M. Bryant, J. Crook, R. Elliot, J. Harrison, C. J .Henty, R. H. Hogg, A. V. Hudson, D. C. Jardine, D. Matthews, J. Mitchell, S. F. Newton, P. Stirling-Aird, M. Trubridge, J. Wheeler, R. E. Youngman.

Falkirk and Clackmannan Districts are indicated by the marginal F and C; S refers to the old Stirling County part of Stirling District and SWP refers to the Perth part of Stirling District.

SYSTEMATIC LIST

RED-THROATED DIVER *Gavia stellata*

F 1 Grangemouth 23 April (DCJ); 1 Skinflats 19 November (DMB)

SWP Pair Loch G 21 April; pair Loch A 23 May; Pair with clutch 2 Loch E, raised 2 young (MT)

BLACK-THROATED DIVER *Gavia arctica*

SWP 1 at Loch A 28 March, pair from 13 April to mid June but no attempt to breed, probably due to low water level, 3 on 1st and 3rd July. Pair on Loch F 16 May, not seen in June (MT); 1 Loch A 16 July (JH)

LITTLE GREBE *Tachybaptus ruficollis*

S Airthrey: 2 on 8 February, maximum 16 on 7 September, 1 on 23 November and 18 December; 5 pairs made 10 attempts but only reared 12 young (MVB)

GREAT CRESTED GREBE *Podiceps cristatus*

F Kinneil: 7 on 7 July, 375 on 22 August, 390 on 2 September, 407 on 14th plus 43 elsewhere on estuary; 20 Skinflats 27 March (DMB MVB AH SFN HR DT MT)

SWP 2 Loch Watston 26 March (DT)

RED-KNECKED GREBE *Podiceps*

F 1 Kinneil 2 September (DMB)

GANNET *Sula bassana*

C 1 juvenile E over Devon at Alva 26 September (SFN)

S 6 juveniles W Airthrey 5 September (DMB); 3 juveniles N over Stirling 30 September (WRB)

SWP 2 adults E Barbush on 27 August (EB)

CORMORANT *Phalacrocorax carbo*

415 Forth Estuary in January (DMB)

F Kinneil: 142 on 8 January, 67 on 5 February, 98 on 14 September, 214 on 14 December (MVB); 60 Skinflats 27 March (DT)

C 74 Kennetpans 8 January, 140 S Alloa Bridge 5 November (MVB CJH)

S Airthrey: 1 on 13 and 24 March, 2 in autumn from 24 August (MVB); Carron Valley Reservoir: 7 on 5 November (CJH)

SWP 7 Lake of Menteith 28 October (RAB)

GREY HERON *Ardea cinerea*

F max 5 Skinflats and 9 Grangemouth 14 September (MVB)

C 17 Tullibody Inch 2 September and 30 on 8 October (DMB WRB)

FLAMINGO sp. *Phoenicopterus* sp.

F 1 Skinflats 17 June (JW). (The majority of flamingoes seen in Scotland that have been identified have been the Chilean species, and hence certainly escapes from captivity. This bird very probably belongs to this category – Editor)

MUTE SWAN *Cygnus olor*

39 Forth Estuary in January (DMB)

F Nested by Union Canal at Falkirk, 4 young on 8 July (DM)

C 12 non-breeders on Devon at Alva in early April, one was colour marked as cygnet on Union Canal, Muiravonside, in August 1987 (SFN); 3 adults and 3 juveniles Cambus Pool 30 March (CJH). Bred Tullibody (Delph Pond) but cygnets apparently killed by vandals (WRB DM); 16 (6 juveniles) Gartmorn dam in late October (SFN)

S Pair hatched 7 at Airthrey but 3 juveniles disappeared in late September (MVB)

SWP 6 cygnets hatched Doune Ponds, only 2 reared (1 death due to bacterial arthritis) (WRB). Nested at Loch Lubnaig, Muir Dam and Loch Watston (DM)

WHOOPER SWAN *Cygnus cygnus*

C 76 by Devon, Alva-Manor Powis in January, last 13 on 26 March (SFN); 61 Gartmorn Dam 28 October and 68 Clackmannan on 29th (WRB SFN)

S 55 Kippen 12 February (SFN); 14 Gargunnock (Shaw of Touch) 18 November (RAB)

SWP 1 Loch Dhu 26 January; 3 Loch Arklet 12 March and 14 on 28th. Loch Chon: 2 in January, max 11 on 22 March and 25 on 28th, 5 on 1 April and 4 May (MT); 16 Lake of Menteith 18 October (RAB). Blairdrummond: 40 on 24 February; 34 Dripend on 11 March, 34 on 22nd, 35 on 24th, 38 on 26th, 40 on 28th, 21 on 31st, 12 on 9 April; 45 Dripend mid December. Thornhill: 86 on 14 January, 52 (Littlewood Wester) on 21st; 49 (Wester Frew) on 11 March; 75 adults (McOrriston) on 15-23 November (CEB MVB RAB WRB DT MT)

PINK-FOOTED GOOSE *Anser brachyrhynchus*
F 113 S Skinflats 19 November, 680 on 14 December (DMB MVB)
C 75 NW Alva 14 April, last (SFN)
S 18 SW Bridge of Allan 09.32 2 February; 85 NW Airthrey 2 May, 09.20 (CJH); 50 E Airthrey 14.30 on 21 November (CJH) *Anser* sp: Kilsyth Ridge 50 W 08.55, 6 SW 09.15, 15 SW 09.29; Myot Hill 30 SW 11.16 5 November (CJH); 15 NE Bridge of Allan 09.05 6 November (CJH)
SWP 5000 feeding and roosting at Thornhill 24 January (EB); 4500 Blairdrummond 24 March; 600 Loch Macanrie 15 April (DT); 7000 Lake of Menteith 31 March and 765 on 2 May (RAB); 120 N Killin 3 May (RAB). Lake of Menteith: big arrival 26 September (per J. Engleby), 200 on 2 October and 1200 on 28th. 940 Thornhill (McOrriston) 18 November; 500 SW Doune 11 October, 5250 Loch Mahaick on 22nd; 2500 Kinbuck 25 November and 850 on 26th (RAB WRB SFN)

WHITE-FRONTED GOOSE *Anser albifrons*
SWP 1 Loch Katrine 26 September (WRB)

GREYLAG GOOSE *Anser anser*
F 1 Skinflats 14 December (MVB)
C 215 Clackmannan 25 November (feeding) and 125 on 14 December, those roosting Gartmorn Dam 2 December probably this group (SFN)
S 8 SW Bridge of Allan 6 November (CJH); 235 roost Loch Coulter 3 November (SFN); 480 Gargunnock (Shaw of Touch) 18 November (RAB)
SWP 1 Lake of Menteith 2 May and 40 (roost) on 28 October (RAB); 178 flighted with Pinkfeet out of Loch Mahaick 22 October (SFN)

SNOW GOOSE *Anser caerulescens*
SWP 1 (white phase) with Pinkfeet Ashfield 25 November (WRB)

CANADA GOOSE *Branta canadensis*
SWP 2 Lake of Menteith 2 May (RAB)

BARNACLE GOOSE *Branta leucopsis*
C 2 Tullibody Inch 8 October (DMB)
SWP 1 Lake of Menteith 2 May (RAB). 2 Ashfield 26 November (WRB)

SHELDUCK *Tadorna tadorna*

2629 Forth Estuary 14 September (DMB)

F Skinflats: 509 on 8 January, 329 on 5 February, 620 on 14 September, 483 on 14 December (MVB). 2546 Kinneil moult flock 30 July (DMB)

C Pair Cambus Pool 30 March and 2 pairs 8 April and 4 June (WRB CJH). 40 Tullibody Inch 2 September and 70 on 5 November (WRB CJH)

WIGEON *Anas penelope*

915 Forth Estuary 14 December (DMB)

F 5 Skinflats 14 September (MVB)

S 40 Loch Coulter 15 January (WRB)

SWP 7 Lake of Menteith 12 March, 8 on 17 December (RAB). 2 Doune Ponds 15 January (first record, WRB)

GADWALL *Anas strepera*

SWP pair Lake of Menteith 2 May (RAB)

TEAL *Anas crecca*

1843 Forth Estuary 5 February (MVB)

F max 70 Skinflats 14 December (MVB). 130 Kinneil 22 August (DT). 800 Grangemouth 30 September (DMB)

C 135 Tullibody Inch 7 January (DMB). 4 Cambus Pool 4 June (CJH)

S 90 Carron Valley Reservoir 3 November (SFN)

MALLARD *Anas platyrhynchos*

1563 Forth Estuary 5 February (DMB)

F Skinflats: 465 on 8 January, 311 on 5 February, 302 on 14 September, 208 on 14 December (MVB)

C 3 pairs and 4 males Cambus Pool 30 March (CJH). At Alva: 50 on flood 16 April; 51 by Devon 21 October, 27 on 7th, 18 on 22 January (SFN). 120 Kennetpans 8 January (MVB)

S Airthrey: max 249 on 8 February, 230 on 7 September, 394 on 10 August, 346 on 18 December. Young broods seen 18 April to 30 June, in 23 broods only 58 out of 158 ducklings fledged (MVB). 71 on Forth at Kippen 19 November (SFN)

PINTAIL *Anas acuta*

F Skinflats: 57 on 3 January and 66 on 8th, 60 on 5 February and 58 on 12th, 71 on 14 December; 13 Kinneil 2 September; 41 Grangemouth 26 February and 9 on 14 September (DMB DVB DCJ JW)

SHOVELER *Spatula clypeata*

C 2 males and 1 female Cambus Pool 8 April, 2 pairs 19 June, may have nested (WRB)

F 1 male Grangemouth 3 June, 1 on 2 September (DMB)

SWP Male Lake of Menteith 2 May (RAB)

POCHARD *Aythya ferina*

S 39 Carron Valley reservoir 3 November (SFN)

SWP 25 Loch Mahaick 30 September (SFN)

TUFTED DUCK *Aythya fuligula*

C Female with c/5 by Devon at Alva 5 July (first attempt in 4 years, SFN)

S Airthrey max: 84 on 14 January, 78 on 8 February, 66 on 15 March, 48 on 23 November, 51 on 18 December; 7-11 pairs, 5 broods, 14 June to 31 July, fledged 21 out of 37 ducklings (MVB). 24 Carron Valley Reservoir 3 November (SFN).

SWP 28 Loch Mahaick 30 September (SFN)

EIDER *Somateria mollissima*

F 3 Kinneil (lagoon) 7 July (DT)

GOLDENEYE *Bucephala clangula*

268 Forth Estuary 8 January (DMB)

F 5 Skinflats 8 January (MVB)

C 35 Tullibody Inch 7 January (DMB)

S 2 Airthrey 9 October (MVB)

SMEW *Mergus albellus*

SWP 1 redhead Lake of Menteith 17 December (RAB)

RED-BREASTED MERGANSER *Mergus serrator*

171 Forth Estuary 5 February (DMB)

F Skinflats: 82 on 8 January and 30 on 14th, 46 on 5 February, 35 on 14 December. 29 Kennetpans 8 January (MVB DCJ)

GOOSANDER *Mergus merganser*

F 2 Skinflats on 8 January, 5 February, 14 September. 6 Kennetpans 8 January (MVB)

C 13 Tullibody Inch 7 January. On Devon: 7 Muckhart on 22 January and 32 on 3 October, 16 Vicars Bridge 26 September, 8 Alva 22 January and 25 November, female with brood 6 Rumbling Bridge 15 May (DMB SFN)

SWP Pair Finglass Reservoir 5 May (CJH)

MARSH HARRIER *Circus aeruginosus*

SWP 1 female/immature flushed from bed of soft rush, Langside Valley (Knaik water) 8 August, left SSE (EB). Female over rabbit warren near Loch Macanrie 25 August (R. K. Pollack)

HEN HARRIER *Circus cyaneus*

S 1 Ballochleam 30 September (CJH)

SWP Of 3 females on breeding territories: one relaid after eggs were robbed, reared 3 young; one laid late and eggs disappeared; one did not lay (EB). At second site, a pair bred close to Loch G (MT). 1 Loch Mahaick 30 September and 1 Sheriffmuir on 28th; 1 male Kinbuck 14 October (MVB SFN). Male Thornhill 7 January, ringtail on 3 December, male on 19th and 22nd (CEB DT)

SPARROWHAWK *Accipiter nisus*

Widespread in square NS79, in 6 of 15 tetrads surveyed (JC)

S Regular Bridge of Allan, Gargunnock, Cambusbarron, Polmaise Castle, also Blairdrummond and Case of Lecropt in SWP (JC). 1 over Bridge of Allan on 19 June was persistently chased and dived at by a Lesser Black-backed Gull (CJH)

BUZZARD *Buteo buteo*

C 1 Dollar and 1 Muckhart 14 April (DMB). 1 Gartmorn Dam 28 October (SFN). 1 Clackmannan (Castlebridge) 25 November (R. Hogg)

S Pair above Gargunnock 30 April (CJH). 2 Ballochleam 30 September (CJH). 1 Airthrey 12 September and 4 on 18th, 1 on 6 October (DMB MVB)

SWP 2 Dunblane (Nether Whiteston) 29 January and 17 September (MVB). 1 Sheriffmuir 17 March; 2 Lecropt 28 October and 1 on 13 November; 3 Loch Lubnaig 21 May (CJH)

GOLDEN EAGLE *Aquila chrysaetos*

SWP Pair near Loch G nested in alternative site (just out of strict recording area) and raised 2 young. Pair Loch D present but did not nest — male is a young bird (MT). Pair near Killin laid 2 eggs but abandoned (WRB)

OSPREY *Pandion haliaetus*

First, 2 on 10 April

KESTREL *Falco tinnunculus*

C 3 pairs on Ochil scarp Menstrie-Balquharn (SFN)

SWP In 3 of 8 NN51 (Strathyre) tetrads (CJH)

MERLIN *Falco columbarius*

F 1 Grangemouth 14 December (MVB). 1 Skinflats 3 April and 19 November (DMB SFN)

C 1 Manorneuk 7 January (DMB)

SWP 1 Loch Lubnaig 27 April (CJH). 1 Sheriffmuir 3 and 28 September (MVB)

HOBBY *Falco subbuteo*

S 1 Airthrey Loch 25 July (DMB). Its passing to the SE caused a flock of House Martins to bunch and avoid. Full description supplied, main features were dark grey upperparts, dark cap and moustache with white face, underparts heavily streaked; wings long, narrow and flexible, tail medium length.

PEREGRINE *Falco peregrinus*

Central Region: 25 territories checked, 17 occupied by pairs and one by a single bird; 12 successful pairs reared 25 young (PS-A JM)

S 1 Pendreich Reservoir 8 August, attacked Lapwings unsuccessfully (RE)

RED GROUSE *Lagopus lagopus*

SWP 10 Meall Glas NN4340 22 January (REY). In 1 of 8 NN51 (Strathyre) tetrads (CJH)

PTARMIGAN *Lagopus mutus*

SWP 1 E side Beinn Cheatlaich NN447326 22 January (REY). 3 Stob a'Choin 4 June, 1 Meall an't Seallaidh 3 September (WRB). None Ben Vane 28 January and 5 June (CJH)

BLACK GROUSE *Tetrao tetrix*

SWP 15 (1 male) Glen Artney 1 January (DMB)

CAPERCAILLIE *Tetrao urogallus*

SWP Female Aberfoyle 24 April, tame enough to be picked up. Male Drumore Wood 14 October (RAB)

RED-LEGGED/CHUKAR PARTRIDGE *Alectoris rufa/chukar*

C 1 found dead (?killed by Sparrowhawk) at Alva 26 April (SFN)

GREY PARTRIDGE *Perdix perdix*

F 10 E Grangemouth 5 February (SFN)

C 8 and 4 Longcarse 5 November (CJH). Alva: 15 by Devon 24 September, 25 (2 coveys) 13 October, 20 at pools 10 November (SFN)

SWP 28 Drip Moss 19 November (SFN)

QUAIL *Coturnix coturnix*

SWP 2 calling Thornhill July-August, also seen (Mr and Mrs Dick, per WRB)

PHEASANT *Phasianus colchicus*

SWP In 1 of 8 NN51 (Strathyre) tetrads (CJH)

MOORHEN Gallinula chloropus

C 4 Cambus Pool 30 March (CJH)

S 14 pairs Airthrey, 27 young fledged hatching 18 April-10 July (MVB). Max Airthrey 33 on 8 February and 29 on 23 November (MVB)

SWP 5 wintered on Allan Water Ashfield-Kinbuck (WRB)

COOT *Fulica atra*

C 13 Cambus Pool 30 March and 8 April, 3 pairs bred (WRB CJH)

S Max Airthrey: 83 8 February and 88 18 December. 24 pairs, fledged 36 young from 39 attempts (hatching 18 April-12 July), poor year due to Mink predation (MVB)

SWP 234 Lake of Menteith 17 December (RAB). 3 pairs Doune Ponds (WRB)

OYSTERCATCHER *Haematopus ostralegus*

835 Forth Estuary 14 September (DMB)

F Max Skinflats 48 on 5 February and 66 on 14 September (MVB)

C 2 in fields at Alva 16 February, 22 on 16 April; 3 pairs Alva-Balquharn, first brood on 3 June (SFN)

S Calling over Airthrey 1 February (SFN), Bridge of Allan 21.30 on 7th (CJH), 10th (JC). 15 Mill Dam 26 March (DT). 35 Airth shore 8 January (MVB)

SWP 2 Thornhill 24 January (CEB). Heard Dunblane 9 February and at Doune Ponds on 17th (MVB WRB). 70 Lake of Menteith 12 March (RAB). 150 Loch Watston 26 March (DT). 100 on ley pasture Blairdrummond 3 July (CJH)

RINGED PLOVER *Charadrius hiaticula*

F 165 Grangemouth 2 September (DMB). 20 Skinflats 8 January and 5 February (MVB). Pair Grangemouth Docks 23 April (DCJ). 5 pairs Lower Earlsburn Reservoir 26 March (DT)

C 2 Cambus Pool 4 June (CJH). 1 Tullibody Inch 2 September (WRB)

SWP 1 heard at night over Ashfield in mid August (WRB)

DOTTEREL *Charadrius morinellus*

SWP 2 at 780m, peat hags, Strathyre 5 May (CJH)

GOLDEN PLOVER *Pluvialis aspricaria*

738 Forth Estuary 14 December (DMB)

F Skinflats: 510 on 3 January and 66 on 8th, 30 on 5 February, 142 on 14 September, 20 on 14 December (MVB DCJ). 150 Kincardine Bridge 23 September (WRB).

C 25 Tullibody Inch 5 November (CJH)

S 1 near Touch Reservoir 3 June (CJH)

SWP 9 Carse of Lecropt 14 October (DT). Pair ben Dubhchreag 2 July; 3 pairs Creag Uchdag 23 June (WRB).

GREY PLOVER *Pluvialis squatarola*

38 Forth Estuary 8 January (DMB)

LAPWING *Vanellus vanellus*

3352 Forth Estuary 8 January (DMB)

F Skinflats: 515 on 8 January, 340 on 5 February, 1330 on 14 September, 107 on 14 December (MVB). 300 Kinneil 3 January (DCJ)

C 820 Longcarse 1 October. 1100 Tullibody Inch 5 November (CJH). 370 Airth shore 8 January (MVB). At Alva max 260 on 26 February, 390 on 21 October, 450 on 14 December, first broods on 27 May (SFN)

KNOT *Calidris canutus*

6280 Forth Estuary 8 January (DMB)

F 300 Kinneil 3 January. 80 Skinflats 8 January (MVB DCJ)

LITTLE STINT *Calidris minuta*

F 5 Grangemouth 14 September (MVB)

C 1 Cambus Pool 14 September (SFN)

DUNLIN *Calidris alpina*

2733 Forth Estuary 14 December (DMB)

F Skinflats: 665 on 8 January, 1250 on 5 February, 320 on 14 September, 1645 on 14 December (MVB)

C 1 Cambus 4 June. 25 Tullibody Inch 5 November (CJH)

RUFF *Philomachus pugnax*

F 1 Grangemouth 2 September (DMB). 11 Kinneil 22 August (DT)

JACK SNIPE *Lymnocryptes minimus*

F 1 Grangemouth 26 February (JW). 1 Kinneil 3 January and 12 March (DCJ)

C 1 in arable, Alva, 7 January (SFN)

SWP 1 Doune Ponds 19 February (WRB)

SNIPE *Gallinago gallinago*

F 30 by Forth at Kincardine Bridge 4 January (DM)

S 1 boggy ground by Touch Reservoir 3 June (CJH)

C 2 in small bog at 612m Blairdenon 16 July. 25 W Alva 20 August; up to 30 Alva Pools late October-end November; 9 Balquharn Burn mouth 30 September (SFN)

WOODCOCK *Scolopax rusticola*

S Scout Head NS7292 10 May

SWP Roding Strathyre 27 April. 1 Glen Finglass 5 July (CJH)

BLACK-TAILED GODWIT *Limosa limosa*

14 Forth Estuary 14 December (DMB)

F Kinneil: 1 on 3 January, 5 on 26 February, 7 on 26th and 9 on 27th March, 19 on 12 April, 8 on 22 August, 16 on 3 September (DCJ DT). 70 Kinneil 30 September (record count, DMB)

BAR-TAILED GODWIT *Limosa lapponica*

285 Forth Estuary 5 February (DMB)

F 229 Kinneil 14 January (DCJ)

WHIMBREL *Numenius phaeopus*

F 1 Kinneil 3 June, 1 on 30 July, 1 on 22 August. 1 Skinflats and 1 Bo'ness 14 September (MVB DMB SFN DT)

CURLEW *Numenius arquata*

1051 Forth Estuary 14 September (DMB)

F 600 Kinneil 30 July (DMB). Skinflats: 58 on 8 January, 135 on 5 February, 207 on 14 September, 74 on 14 December (MVB)

S Calling, NE, at 19.20 Bridge of Allan 15 March (CJH). 2 W, high and calling, Bridge of Allan 09.30 23 July (CJH). 135 Airth shore 8 January (MVB)

SWP 55 Drip Moss 11 March and 2 Lake of Menteith on 12th (MVB RAB). Widespread and displaying Braeleny 27 March; in 1 of 8 NN51 (Strathyre) tetrads (CJH). Passage SW Dunblane 18 June to mid-August (MVB)

SPOTTED REDSHANK *Tringa erythropus*

F 1 Skinflats 3 January (DCJ)

REDSHANK *Tringa totanus*

2503 Forth Estuary 14 September (DMB)

F Skinflats: 635 on 8 January, 800 on 5 February, 400 on 14 September, 865 on 14 December (MVB). 120 Kincardine Bridge 23 September (WRB)

C 30 Tullibody Inch 5 November (CJH). Pair bred Cambus Pool (WRB). By Devon at Alva from 1 April, 4 at Alva Pools early July, fledged juveniles seen from 5 July (SFN)
S 2 near Touch Reservoir 10 May and 1 on 3 June (CJH)
SWP 1 Lake of Menteith 12 March (RAB)

GREENSHANK *Tringa nebularia*
F 8 Grangemouth 2 September (DMB). 1 Skinflats 8th and 14th January, 27 March, 14 September (MVB DCJ). 4 Kinneil 22 August and 6 on 3 September (DT). 1 Kincardine Bridge 23 September (WRB)
C 1 Cambus Pool 26 August and 2 September (WRB SFN)
S 2 Pendreich Reservoir 8 August, left SE (RE)

GREEN SANDPIPER *Tringa ochropus*
C 1 Cambus Pool 12 and 26 August and 2 September (WRB SFN)

COMMON SANDPIPER *Actitis hypoleucos*
F 6 Kinneil 30 July, 1 on 14 September (DMB SFN)
C 2 Glendevon 30 July (DMB). Last Cambus 2 September (WRB). First by Devon at Alva 15 April, 4 pairs on 2.5 km river, left by 20 July (SFN)
S 3 Touch reservoirs 29 April (DT)
SWP In 4 of 8 NN51 (Strathyre) tetrads (CJH). 1 Doune Ponds 9 April, bred there (WRB)

TURNSTONE *Arenaria interpres*
106 Forth Estuary 8 January (DMB)

ARCTIC SKUA *Stercorarius parasiticus*
F 8 Kinneil 2 September (DMB)

BLACK-HEADED GULL *Larus ridibundus*
C 485 Alva 22 September (SFN)

COMMON GULL *Larus canus*
C 100 Menstrie January-February (SFN)
S 1220 roosting Loch Coulter 3 November (SFN)

LESSER BLACK-BACKED GULL *Larus fuscus*
F 2 Skinflats 3 January (DCJ)
S First Bridge of Allan 17 February (JC)
SWP 173 Thornhill 18 November (RAB)

SANDWICH TERN *Sterna sandvicensis*

F 7 Grangemouth 23 April (DCJ). Abundant over Forth off Grangemouth on 8 August (CJH). 40 Kinneil 2 September (DMB).

COMMON TERN *Sterna hirundo*

F 62 incubating birds Grangemouth Docks 3 June (DMB)

ARCTIC TERN *Sterna paradisaea*

F 1 Kinneil 2 September (DMB)

GUILLEMOT *Uria aalge*

F 24 Skinflats 8 January and 10 on 14th, 51 on 5 February, 34 on 14 December; 30 Grangemouth 23 April (MVB DCJ)

C 1 W over Devon at Alva 10 December (SFN)

S 1 flying W Airthrey 13 December and 1 Fintry on 15th (DMB RAB MT). 3 Dunmore 8 January (MVB)

SWP 1 Loch Dhu 9 November; 1 Lake of Menteith on 18th; 1 Gartmore and 3 Lake of Menteith 17 December; 1 Trossachs on 18th; recently dead birds at Inversnaid 18 November and at Loch Arklet on 22 December (RAB MT)

STOCK DOVE *Columba oenas*

C 5 Cambus (Orchard Farm) 2 September (WRB)

S 2 Airthrey 15 May (MVB)

SWP 1 singing Blairdrummond 18 July (JC)

WOODPIGEON *Columba palumba*

F 200 Kinneil 12 February (DCJ)

COLLARED DOVE *Streptopelia decaocto*

C 45 in stubble Sauchie 5 September (M. Still). 13 Alva 26 November (SFN)

S 29 Airthrey 19 January, 32 on 8 February (MVB).

CUCKOO *Cuculus canorus*

C First Alva 9 May (SFN)

SWP In 2 of 8 NN51 (Strathyre) tetrads (CJH). 3 Menteith Hills 20 May; 2 Flanders Moss 11 June (WRB)

BARN OWL *Tyto alba*

F 1 Lathallan 2 January (JW)

TAWNY OWL *Strix aluco*

SWP Poor year for breeding success (HR). Calling Strathyre 27 April (CJH)

SHORT-EARED OWL *Asio flammeus*

F 1 Grangemouth 14 December (MVB). 1 Kinneil 5 February (SFN)

SWP 1 Ashfield mid-September (WRB)

SWIFT *Apus apus*

C At Tillicoultry and Dollar 10 May; Alva on 14th (SFN)

S 2 Bridge of Allan 5 May, 6 on 10th (DMB CJH). July: 50 on 18th, 45 on 20th, 35 on 23rd. August: 35 on 1st, 45 on 2nd, 35 on 6th, last on 11th (CJH)

SWP 13 Dunblane 12 May, 60 by 22nd, last 2 on 20 August (MVB)

KINGFISHER *Alcedo atthis*

C 1 Crook of Devon 22 January, 2 in early April; 2 Muckhart mid-April — 1 carrying fish on 19th (DMB). 3 juveniles ringed Rumbling Bridge-Crook of Devon in mid-September retrapped Vicars Bridge-Dollar in next 3 weeks. 1 at Alva April, August, October, November (SFN). Pair Cambus 2 September (WRB). In 1988 pair with 3 young in June on Devon below Dollar (AH)

S 1 with fish Carron Glen (NS7784) in summer (per NCC). Singles Airthrey 19 May and 24-25 August (MVB). Twice in summer on river at Bridge of Allan, also 1 flew into window on 18 August, photographed and released (JC)

SWP 1 at Sandmartin colony on Teith, Lecropt, 14 July (JC). 1 Ashfield July and October. 1 Doune Ponds 20-24 October (WRB)

GREEN WOODPECKER *Picus viridis*

C 2 broods fledged on Ochil slopes Tillicoultry-Harviestoun. 1 brood fledged Alva 11-15 July. 1 Blairhall (Rumbling Bridge) 28 September (SFN)

SWP 1 Anie Glen (Strathyre) 6 June (CJH). 1 Glendevon church 20 April (SFN). Occasional Doune Ponds (?rather scarce WRB)

GREAT SPOTTED WOODPECKER *Dendrocopus major*

S calling above Gargunnock 30 April (CJH). Drumming at Airthrey 15-28 March and pair with 2 fledged young 17 June (MVB SFN)

SKYLARK *Alauda arvensis*

F 80 Kinneil on 14 January (DCJ)

SWP Widespread and singing Braeleny 27 March; in 5 of 8 NN51 (Strathyre) tetrads (CJH). 30 Kinbuck 8 October (MVB)

SANDMARTIN *Riparia riparia*

C 250 Gartmorn Dam 2 April (WRB). 10 at Devon (Alva) 8 April (SFN)

S First Airthrey 29 March, 15 on 30th, 40 on 25 April (DMB MVB CJH)
SWP 80 Lake of Menteith and 80 Barbush 31 March (WRB DT)

SWALLOW *Hirundo rustica*
C 1 Alva 16 April (SFN)
S 1 Blairlogie 18 April; 1 Airthrey on 22nd (DMB MVB). 5 Gartmorn 2 April; 2 Stirling 13 October (WRB). 4 SW Airthrey 6 October and 1 on 10 November (DMB)
SWP 2 Lake of Menteith 22 April (DT)

HOUSE MARTIN *Delichon urbica*
C 3 Glendevon 7 May (DMB). First Alva 18 May (SFN)
S 1 Bridge of Allan 28 October (DMB)
SWP 1 Dunblane 6 May, late influx 22 June (MVB)

TREE PIPIT Anthus trivialis
S Singing Scout Head 10 May (CJH). 2 Bridge of Allan 21 May (DMB)

MEADOW PIPIT *Anthus pratensis*
F 400 Skinflats 14 September (MVB)
S 140 Sheriffmuir 3 September, 5 on 9 December (MVB)
SWP Widespread and singing Braeleny 27 March (CJH). In 7 of 8 NN51 (Strathyre) tetrads (CJH)

ROCK PIPIT *Anthus petrosus*
F 1 Kinneil 14 January (DCJ)

GREY WAGTAIL *Motacilla cinerea*
S 1 Airthrey 14 June to October (MVB)
SWP In 6 of 8 NN51 (Strathyre) tetrads (CJH). Successful breeding season in Trossachs (HR).

PIED WAGTAIL *Motacilla alba*
S 150 at pre-roost, Airthrey 18.30 on 14 September (CJH). 5 flying at moderate height Ballochleam ridge 15.20 30 September (CJH)
SWP In 4 out 8 NN51 (Strathyre) tetrads (CJH). Successful breeding season in Trossachs (HR)

WAXWING *Bombycilla garrulax*
F 6 Polmont 19 February (JW)
C 25 by A977 at Clackmannan 1 January (JW)
S 75 Airthrey 17 January and 2 on 20th (DMB MVB AVH SFN), 10 on 17 February (JC). 1988: 15 feeding on yews in Stirling 24 December (JH).

WREN *Troglodytes troglodytes*

SWP In 6 of 8 NN51 (Strathyre) tetrads (CJH)

ROBIN *Erithacus rubecula*

S Singing strongly Airthrey 14 August but not Mine Wood (CJH)

SWP In 3 of 8 NN51 (Strathyre) tetrads (CJH)

REDSTART *Phoenicurus phoenicurus*

C 1 fledged juvenile seen N of Alva 15 July and 2 on 16th (AVH SFN)

SWP In 6 of 8 NN51 (Strathyre) tetrads (CJH). At Trossachs nestbox colony 54 pairs reared 275 young (HR). Male Doune Ponds 17 August; 1 Sheriffmuir 20 and 27 August (WRB)

WHINCHAT *Saxicola rubetra*

F 2 Grangemouth 14 September (MVB)

C A few in post breeding dispersal onto arable fields round Alva, from 16 August to 5 September (AVH SFN).

S 1 Bridge of Allan 7 May (DMB)

SWP In 2 of 8 NN51 (Strathyre) tetrads (CJH)

STONECHAT *Saxicola torquata*

F 2 Kinneil 14 December (MVB)

C Fledged juvenile Alva 18 August and 2 from 25th until 7 September (AVH SFN)

SWP 2 pairs Menteith Hills 20 May (WRB). Male Frandy 23 April (MN-T)

WHEATEAR *Oenanthe oenanthe*

F 1 Greenland form Kinneil 13 May (DCJ)

C 4 Glendevon 16 April (DMB). Post breeding at Alva 11 July to 25 August (AVH SFN)

S 1 Pendreich Reservoir 1 April (DT)

SWP 2 males Braeleny 27 March; in 5 of 8 NN51 (Strathyre) tetrads, newly fledged young on 5 July (CJH)

RING OUZEL *Turdus torquatus*

S 1 Touch Reservoir 10 May (CJH)

SWP Singing Glen Kendrum 9 April (RAB). 2 pairs An Caisteil 22 July; 2 pairs Creag Uchdeag 23 June (WRB)

FIELDFARE *Turdus pilaris*

C 25 Alva 12 March and 80 on 19 November (AVH SFN)

S 23 SW Kilsyth Ridge 5 November (CJH). At Airthrey 4 W on 12 October, 300 W on 30th; 650 W on 1 November and 250 W on 23rd (MVB). 15 feeding on fallen apples in garden at Bridge of Allan late December (CJH)

SWP 100 Thornhill 1 April; 300 Braes of Doune 19 November and 500 at Thornhill (AVH SFN)

REDWING *Turdus iliacus*

S 20 W Airthrey 12 October and 130 W on 30th (MVB)

SWP 50 Loch Ruskie 21 January (MVB). 4 wintered Bechwood Park to early March (WRB). First Ashfield 3 October; 20 Aberfoyle on 11th (WRB). Parties widespread Callendar 8 October (RAB). 200 Braes of Doune 19 November (AVH SFN)

MISTLE THRUSH *Turdus viscivorus*

S 1 feeding on Stranvesia berries in Bridge of Allan late December, bush stripped by early January (CJH)

SWP 35 at edge of forest Loch Mahaick 30 September (AVH SFN)

GRASSHOPPER WARBLER *Locustella naevia*

C 1 singing Cambus Pool 19 June (WRB). 1 Alva 10 and 11 May (AVH SFN)

S 1 singing through summer by river at Bridge of Allan (JC). Pair (song and display) by A811 at Kippen 3 May, song heard through summer (JH)

SEDGE WARBLER *Acrocephalus schoenobaenus*

F 2 Grangemouth 14 September (MVB)

C 2-3 pairs Cambus Pool (WRB). First by Devon at Alva 5 May; 10 pairs Alva pools in June, fledged young seen 26 June (AVH SFN)

S 1 Airthrey 4 May (MVS)

SWP Pair Doune Ponds, 3 pairs Ashfield railway cutting (WRB)

WHITETHROAT *Sylvia communis*

C First Alva 20 May, more nesting than in previous 4 years, last on 1 October (AVH SFN)

S Singing Airthrey 17 May-5 June (MVB)

GARDEN WARBLER *Sylvia borin*

S Singing Airthrey 12 May-8 June (MVB)

SWP In 3 of 8 NN51 (Strathyre) tetrads (CJH)

BLACKCAP *Sylvia atricapilla*

S Male Airthrey 18 April, singing 2-19 May (MVB). 1 singing Plean Estate 17 July (WRB)

SWP Singing Strathyre (N of Loch Lubnaig) 3 July (CJH)

WOOD WARBLER *Phylloscopus sibilitrax*

S Singing Scout Head 10 May (CJH)

SWP Singing Brig o'Turk 5 May, Dunblane (Dykedale Wood) 3 June

(MVB). In 3 of 8 NN51 (Strathyre) tetrads (CJH). Probably more numerous around Callander, even in conifers (WRB)

CHIFF CHAFF *Phylloscopus collybita*
S Singing Airthrey 2 and 7 April and until 7 August with 3 on 19 July, last on 7 September (MVB CJH). 1 Bridge of Allan 18 April (DMB). 2 Plean Estate 17-21 July (WRB)
SWP Singing Lake of Menteith 27 and 31 March and Dunblane (Dykedale Wood) 8 April (MVB DT). 1 Doune Ponds 10 September-14 November (WRB)

WILLOW WARBLER *Phylloscopus trochilus*
C 1 Gartmorn Dam 2 April (WRB). First Alva 22 April (AVH SFN)
S 2 singing Airthrey 12 April (MVB)
SWP 2 Lake of Menteith 15 April (DT). In 6 of 8 NN51 (Strathyre) tetrads (CJH)

GOLDCREST *Regulus regulus*
SWP In 3 of 8 NN51 (Strathyre) tetrads (CJH)

SPOTTED FLYCATCHER *Muscicapa striata*
S 2 Bridge of Allan 21 May (DMB). 1 Airthrey 5 June (MVB)
SWP Family party Dunblane 20 August (MVB)

PIED FLYCATCHER *Ficedula hypoleuca*
S Male visited nest boxes in Hermitage Wood, Airthrey (R. Johnson)
SWP At Trossachs nestbox colony 80 pairs reared 440 young (HR)

LONG-TAILED TIT *Aegithalos caudatus*
S 15 Airthrey 20 June (MVB)

RED-BACKED SHRIKE *Lanius excubitor*
SWP Male at Glen Ogle bealach 26 May, perched on fence by cottages (B. Cowan)

GREAT GREY SHRIKE *Lanius excubitor*
S 1 Gargunnock 25 March (DCJ)

JAY *Garrulus glandarius*
C 1 Dollar 25 May (DMB). (Few breeding season records for Hillfoots – Editor)

MAGPIE *Pica pica*
C 11 Alva 13 October (AVH SFN)

JACKDAW *Corvus monedula*
SWP In 1 of 8 NN51 (Strathyre) tetrads (CJH)

ROOK *Corvus frugilegus*

C 5000 (with Jackdaws) roosting Gartmorn Dam 22 October (AVH SFN)

S Rookeries: Myretoun 57, Witches Craig 32, 29 April (CJH). 18 Bridge of Allan N (deciduous part) 9 May

SWP Not recorded in summer in NN51 (Strathyre)

CARRION CROW *Corvus corone*

S 1 Hooded Crow Blairlogie 16 February (AVH SFN)

SWP 1 Hooded Crow Lake of Menteith 12 March (RAB) In breeding season seen in all 8 tetrads in Strathyre square NN51, CJH noted 22 pure black Carrion Crows, 7 hybrids and 1 apparently pure Hooded Crow.

RAVEN *Corvus corax*

C 2 Alva 19 August and 1 September (AVH SFN)

SWP At least 10 (probably 12) territories occupied out of 14, 8 pairs successful 5 of which reared 11 young (PS-A). 1 over Callander Golf Course 27 March (CJH). 1 Braes of Doune 22 October (AVH SFN). 2 Druim Meadhoin 2 August. 2 Lag a'Phuil (Strathyre) 5 May (CJH)

HOUSE SPARROW *Passer domesticus*

S 200 in stubble Cornton 18 August (MVB). Scores roosting in Virginia Creeper in mid autumn, Bridge of Allan, deserted it when leaves fell (CJH)

TREE SPARROW *Passer montanus*

C 5 Cambus 2 September; 5 Longcarse 1 October (WRB CJH)

S Colonies by Forth at Drip Bridge and Cambusbarron (high hedges by limekiln) (JC)

CHAFFINCH *Fringilla coelebs*

S 195 Airthrey 30 January, 150 on 9 February and 200 on 7 September (MVB AVH SFN)

SWP 400 Thornhill 7 January (DT). In 6 of 8 NN51 (Strathyre) tetrads (CJH)

BRAMBLING *Fringilla montifringilla*

SWP 2 with Chaffinches Thornhill 7 January (DT). 3 (1 male in breeding plumage) on ploughed land Kinbuck 23 April (JH)

GREENFINCH *Carduelis chloris*

C 40 Alva 22 August and 80 on 6 September (AVH SFN)

SWP 75 Dunblane, Dykedale Wood, 18 November (MVB)

GOLDFINCH *Carduelis carduelis*

C 125 Alva 9 February and up to 45 until mid-month (AVH SFN)

S 20 Airthrey 23 February, 24 on 12 April and 15 on 19 October (MVB CJH AVH SFN)

F Up to 30 Polmont January-March (JW)

SISKIN *Carduelis spinus*

C Pair in plantation at Dollar (Maidens Well) 1 June (AVH SFN)

S Pair last seen at nuts Bridge of Allan 26 April (CJH)

SWP 40 Dunblane, Dykedake Wood, 23 September (MVB). In 4 of 8 NN51 (Strathyre) tetrads (CJH)

LINNET *Carduelis cannabina*

F 200 Skinflats 3 January (DCJ)

C 60 Cambus 2 September and 60 Longcarse 5 November (WRB CJH)

S 75 Blairlogie 10 August (AVH SFN)

TWITE *Carduelis flavirostris*

C At Alva, pair by Devon 12 and 16 May and in garden on 18th (AVH SFN)

S 4 by sheepfank at Lower Touch Reservoir 10 May (CJH)

SWP 20 Kirkton Glen, 540m, 10 January. 2-3 pairs Fin Glen (Loch Tay) 23 June (WRB). 3 Lake of Menteith 2 May (RAB). On July 5: Finglass Reservoir, 2 NN525093, 2 at NN530092 — on pasture with stone walls; Gleann nam Meann, NN523125, 2 with 2 juveniles, pasture near sheepfank (CJH)

REDPOLL *Carduelis flammea*

C Pair in plantation Dollar (Maidens Well) 1 June (AVH SFN, sole record)

SWP In one tetrad (Calair Burn) in Strathyre (CJH)

CROSSBILL *Loxia curvirostra*

SWP 13 Lake of Menteith 12 February and 1 on 12 March (RAB)

HAWFINCH *Coccothraustes coccothraustes*

SWP 1 Doune (Moray Park) 31 January and probably in April (WRB)

LAPLAND BUNTING *Calcarius lapponicus*

F 1 Kinneil 12 February (DCJ)

SNOW BUNTING *Plectrophenax nivalis*

S 1 Stronend 12 February (AVH SFN). 1 Meikle Bin 19 November (WRB)

SWP 1 Glen Kendrum 29 January (RAB). 2 females on peat hags at 575m Ben Vane 28 January (CJH). 6 Sgiath Chuil NN464312 22 January (REY). 2 Meall ant'Seallaidh 10 January (WRB)

YELLOWHAMMER *Emberiza citrinella*

S 25 roosting in Pyracanthra Airthrey 17.30 on 21 February (CJH). 40 Kippen, Littlewood Wester, 21 January. 3 singing Airthrey late June (MVB)

SWP 40 Blairdrummond Moss 21 January (MVB)

REED BUNTING *Emberiza schoeniclus*

F 15 Kinneil 30 September (DMB)

C 3-4 pairs Cambus Pool (WRB). 5 by Devon at Alva 12 March (AVH SFN)

SWP 24 with Yellowhammers, Blairdrummond Moss 21 January (MVB). Pairs Doune Ponds and Ashfield (WRB)

CORN BUNTING *Miliaria calandra*

F 5 singing Skinflats-Airth 26 April (DCJ)

Species known to be in the area but for which no notes have been received:

BEAN GOOSE *Anser fabalis*
HERRING GULL *Larus argentatus*
GREAT BLACK-BACKED GULL *Larus marinus*
FERAL ROCK DOVE *Columba livia*
LONG-EARED OWL *Asio Otus*
DIPPER *Cinclus cinclus*
DUNNOCK *Prunella modularis*
BLACKBIRD *Turdus merula*
SONG THRUSH *Turdus philomenos*
LONG-TAILED TIT *Aegithalos caudatus*
COAT TIT *Parus ater*
BLUE TIT *Parus caeruleus*
GREAT TIT *Parus major*
TREECREEPER *Certhia familiaris*
STARLING *Sturnus vulgaris*
BULLFINCH *Pyrrhula pyrrhula*

BOOK REVIEW

Birds and the North Sea : 10th anniversary publication of the North Sea Bird Club. Editor S. M. D. Alexander. 1990. 160pp. Copies available at £4 from Ben Thompson, BP Patent Development, Forben Industrial Estate, Dyce, Aberdeen.

A celebratory publication of some dozen articles on key aspects of the knowledge and observations of a very active membership of 'oilmen' and others. The Club has built up a sizeable data bank backed by Aberdeen University resources in recording, validation and analysis. The contributions cover geography and hydrology, climate and weather, marine mammals, bats, fish, insects, in addition to the bird studies – on mortality patterns, movements, and a 50 page check/status listing.

BOOK REVIEWS

The Annals of Kinross-shire 490-1870. Editors Hon. R. and A. Moncreiff. Fossoway Community Council. 1990. 130pp ISBN 0 9515597 0 2. £3.75.

This is a fascinating 'Annual Register' like local history resource, a rich spread of accounts of national events like Mary Queen of Scots escape from Loch Leven Castle, local occasions strange, humorous and tragic, and memorable local characters – a sampling of life over a 500 year span. Part I to 1861 is reprinted, and now lovingly illustrated, from the original cuttings scrapbook of the historian Dr Ebenezer Henderson of Muckhart's weekly column to the Kinross-shire Advertiser – now the *Fife Herald.* Part 2 is of similar writings of R. L. Wright and Dr W. Haldane.

First published in 1870, reprinted in 1912, the text had been out of print for many years when the Community Council were loaned the scrapbook by the Hon. Mrs Vida Young and became enthused with a plan to enrich the text with relevant archival maps, photographs and drawings available in Tullibole Castle, Blairadam House and elsewhere, and present it at a modest price to promote interest in the area's heritage. They certainly succeeded here in nicely producing, with the help of their local banks and library, this vivid picture of Kinross-shire, 'packaged' in an eye catching market-place cover, at an attractive promotional price.

L. Corbett

Global Rivers Environmental Education Programme : an outreach project, Department of Natural Resources, University of Michigan. A workshop report by Kate Sankey, 1989. 16pp. Scottish Environmental Education Council (SEEC) occasional paper no. 2, with Central Region Environmental Education Forum (CREEF).

From a schools project in a densely populated and highly industrial area of Michigan, rivers environment studies developed regionally in the USA, then spread abroad till by 1989 there are teams of students running workshops in four continents and 20 countries.

Green : the Global Rivers Environmental Education Network volume 1 no. 2. University of Michigan, December 1989. 16pp.

An example of the Green Project with notes on highlights of Green activities in various countries including Bristol – the Avon, Aberdeen – the Don and Dee, and Stirling – the Forth.

MOORLAND BIRDS ON THE CAMPSIE FELLS, TOUCH HILLS AND WEST OCHIL HILLS, STIRLING: HABITATS, DISTRIBUTION AND NUMBERS

J. Calladine, S. Dougill, N. Harding and D. A. Stroud

INTRODUCTION

The Campsie Fells, Touch Hills and west Ochil Hills are areas of moorland, peat-bog and sheep-walk in central Scotland, moderately small and discrete, and surrounded by urban or agricultural ground. Although close to centres of population, there was a lack of quantitative information on birds. Recently, a high level of afforestation has resulted in extensive habitat loss and widespread degradation of vegetation as a consequence of overgrazing by sheep. Further losses of moorland have occurred in the past as a result of flooding to create reservoirs.

In order to plan conservation of remaining moorland areas, this survey of moorland birds was undertaken by the Moorland Bird Study of the Nature Conservancy Council's (NCC) Chief Scientist Directorate during April-July 1987. Its aim was to assess bird populations of survey sites, with emphasis on moorland breeding waders, and to relate the distribution and relative numbers of breeding birds to habitat structure and topography. The results have been published in two internal NCC reports (Calladine *et al.* 1987; Harding *et al.* 1988); this paper summarises the main results and subsequent analyses.

Previous moorland bird surveys have shown that breeding waders such as Golden Plover, Dunlin, Curlew and Snipe have very distinct habitat preferences (Reed 1985; Stroud *et al.* 1987; Haworth 1987). Certain vegetation types, such as bog pools, mixed age heather *(Calluna vulgaris)* stands, and a mosaic of vegetation types are generally preferred, whilst other features such as areas dominated by dry deer-grass *Tricophorum cespitosum),* and dry uniform age heather are generally avoided. Within a general pattern there are also ecological differences between species, e.g. very wet flushes seem to be of greater overall importance for Snipe than for some other waders such as Golden Plover. Dunlin, however, show a particularly strong affinity for wet areas of bog pools within generally undamaged blanket bogs.

Recent work has demonstrated that consistent features of habitat selection can be used to obtain information on the likely quality, as breeding habitat, of areas for which habitat or topographic information is available, but for which there have been no direct bird surveys (Campbell 1985). Such work has been undertaken by NCC in Caithness and Sutherland, where landform features (identifiable direct from OS topographic maps) were found to relate to densities of a number of species of breeding waders (Stroud *et al.* 1987).

This paper presents information on vegetation and erosion of the moorlands and investigates the patterns of distribution of the moorland breeding birds with respect to topography. It also indicates which landform types would be generally likely to hold high numbers of breeding birds.

EXTENT OF SURVEY AND METHODS USED

Ten sites were surveyed (Figure 1), representing the range of moorland landforms and habitats present in the area. A high proportion (c40%) of the non-afforested moorland was surveyed in the Campsie Fells/Touch Hills with two additional sites in the west Ochil Hills. The main vegetation types represented were *Calluna-Eriophorum* blanket bog, *Calluna* damp heath, *Calluna* dry heath, species — poor *Agrostis-Festuca* grassland, *Nardus* grassland and *Juncus* dominated mire. Additionally there were smaller areas of flush communities along or near natural watercourses. Many vegetation communities had been altered by intense grazing pressure. The predominant land-use of the sites was sheep grazing. No peat-cutting was in evidence, but on some sites very intensive moor-gripping (drainage channels) had occurred. Nearly three-quarters of all sites were adjacent to existing conifer plantations, and a few other areas surveyed were subject to forestry applications.

Details of the sites, their area and location are given in Table 1, they ranged from 240m to 705m above sea level, and of average size 601ha (range 178 to 707ha) .

Methods of Bird Survey

The survey method used was a standardised transect procedure described by Stroud *et al.* (1987) which allows survey of large tracts of land for identification of important breeding areas. For most moorland bird species, finding the nest of any given pair is too difficult for this to be a feasible means of population counting over the large areas which have to be surveyed. Observation of adult birds in their nesting territories thus has to be the principal basis of census. A territory mapping method was used, whereby a site was visited several times (at least four) in the course of the breeding season. A pair of observers walked a series of transect lines across the site 200m apart; thus no part of the site was more than 100m from an observer. Once decided the transect pattern was adhered to, with observers on subsequent visits using the same transects as on the first visit but reversing the direction of walking them on each occasion. Bearings were taken frequently to ensure that the same transect lines were used on each visit.

Weather can adversely affect the number and behaviour of birds seen. Recording was not attempted if there was a strong wind (>Force 5, or even less in exposed areas), rain, low cloud or fog. On each visit, observers recorded the birds seen from the transect lines. All sightings were mapped, using a code (including details of behaviour) onto 1:10,000 maps in the field. Any double recording (i.e. when both observers saw and recorded the same bird during a transect) was corrected at the end of each line walked. At the end of each day a single composite map was produced. The sightings were then transferred to a summary site map for each species. At the end of the season it was thus possible to determine the number of territorial pairs of each species on each site from the clusters of species on the summary maps. Breeding densities are expressed in this report as pairs per km^2. These will be minimum values, especially for species such as Snipe and probably also Dunlin.

Visits were undertaken during the period 16 April-3 July 1987. All sites were visited four times, with seven having an additional fifth visit. The timing and range of visits was planned so as to encompass periods of territory establishment, nesting and incubation and fledging. However, species differ in detectability during summer, and different species have peaks of detectability at different times of the breeding season (e.g. Reed and Langslow 1985).

Vegetation Recording

At the same time as the bird survey, a number of habitat features were also recorded. Vegetation of sites was recorded using upland vegetation categories devised by Birds and Ratcliffe (1980): the most abundant are listed in Table 4. Botanical descriptions are given by Birks and Ratcliffe (1980).

Peat Erosion Recording

Degree and extent of peat erosion was mapped for each site according to a six point scale. In the absence of a generally accepted scale of peat erosion, categories given in Table 5 have been devised and used over the last two years, combining information on physical structure (depth of gullies), vegetation communities, position of water-table and water flow across the peatland.

BIRD DISTRIBUTION AND DENSITIES: RESULTS AND DISCUSSION

Numbers of birds found breeding on each survey site are given in Table 2, whilst densities of waders are shown in Table 3. In all cases these densities will be minima. Presented densities will also underestimate density of birds in 'good' habitats since sites included areas of both 'good' and 'bad' habitat. Local densities for many species were considerably higher than when expressed across a whole site. For some species such as Meadow Pipit, Skylark and Red Grouse, the method does not allow an accurate estimation of numbers, and these are shown accordingly in Table 2. Numbers of breeding bird species on the sites ranged from five to eleven. Other birds were undoubtedly breeding in the general area, but outside the specific sites surveyed (e.g. Mallard, Teal, Peregrine). Abundance of each of the main breeding species, and other information on their occurrence in the area are summarised below.

Curlew

Curlew were the most abundant breeding wader, with breeding occurring on all sites. Densities ranged from 0.66-3.11 pairs/km^2 (mean 1.56; sd 0.86 pairs/km^2). Breeding density of Curlews ranks moderately in comparison to other moorland areas studied. Densities are significantly higher than on Caithness and Sutherland peatlands (where mean density is 0.51 pairs/km^2: Stroud *et al.* 1987), whilst being lower than more southerly areas in the Pennines and Co. Durham (NCC unpublished). The present density is similar however, to that found over considerable areas of the North York Moors (mean of 1.45 pairs/km^2: NCC/NYMNP unpublished).

Golden Plover

Golden Plovers bred on eight sites, at densities from 0.28-1.45 pairs/km^2 (mean of all sites 0.49; sd 0.43 pairs/km^2). Generally, densities of breeding Golden Plovers were low. Previous surveys have found significantly higher densities on the limestone grasslands, blanket bogs and moorlands of the Penines, southern Uplands and northern England (Ratcliffe 1976; NCC unpublished). Densities are also lower than those found on the Caithness and Sutherland peatlands (Stroud *et al.* 1987), although densities on some of the present sites approach those found further north in Perthshire (NCC unpublished).

Lapwing

Lapwing bred on four sites and were present, although not proved breeding, on a fifth. Breeding densities ranged from 0.15-0.42 pairs/km^2 (mean of all sites 0.11; sd 0.15 pairs/km^2). Lapwing are not typical moorland breeding waders, but tend to be associated with areas of low intensity agricultural ground or abandoned hill pastures within moorland. Comparison of densities with other moorland surveys or areas is thus problematic since such comparison implicitly assumes equivalent areas of suitable habitat. This is not always the case. Higher densities of breeding Lapwings are found on the marginal agricultural ground just outwith the moorlands surveyed, but on areas potentially afforestable. Studies elsewhere have indicated that a mosaic of different habitats is important, since different areas are used at different times of the breeding season (e.g. Galbraith 1987).

Snipe

Snipe were found on six sites and occurred at densities of 0.19-0.45 pairs/km^2 (mean of all sites 0.28; sd 0.10 pairs/km^2). Snipe present particular census problems due to their cryptic breeding behaviour (Green 1985; Smith 1981), thus densities presented here will be minimum in all cases, and 'real' numbers will undoubtedly be considerably higher. Comparison of average breeding densities with other areas presents difficulties due to differing census procedures, however it appears that densities in the Campsies area surveyed are higher than those found with the same methods on the Caithness and Sutherland peatlands, whilst slightly lower than in Pennine areas and the southern Uplands. Within all areas however, distribution of breeding Snipe is strongly determined by availability of suitable wet flushes, damp rushy pastures and other boggy areas, such that overall comparisons are perhaps of little value.

Dunlin

Dunlin were found on two sites with one pair located on the Cort-ma-law site and two pairs on Hart Hill. Both sites have a history of occupation by Dunlin (J. Mitchell). The latter site included some of the wettest, relatively un-eroded blanket peat in the area (Table 5), although extensive pool systems were absent. Recent extensive moor gripping (drainage channels) had occurred in the area containing Dunlin which may have adversely affected them. Dunlin have a scattered distribution within British uplands and tend to show a strong affinity for the wettest peatlands, especially where there are well developed pool systems. There are few previous breeding records of Dunlin in this area of central Scotland, and Thom (1986) considered that they bred only irregularly here. This scarcity makes protection of known breeding areas important.

Common Sandpiper

Single pairs of Common Sandpiper were present at two sites, and in both cases were associated with moorland streams.

Wheatear

Wheatears bred on nine sites at densities from 0.14-0.84 pairs/km^2 (mean of all sites 0.41; sd 0.27 pairs/km^2).

Peregrine

Peregrines were seen hunting over two sites, and the escarpment cliffs are an important breeding area (Mitchell and Broad 1987). The maintenance of adequate feeding habitat close to these nesting sites is important.

Red Grouse

Red Grouse are strongly associated with heather moorlands and bred on all survey sites. High relative densities were found on three sites, and lower on others. Survey methods employed do not give good quantitative estimates of Red Grouse numbers, so it is not possible to assess their significance here with respect to other areas.

VEGETATION RECORDING

After vegetation maps for each site had been prepared, a 200m x 200m grid was overlain on each site map, and presence of each vegetation community was recorded within each 200m x 200m 'quadrat'. The abundance and relative proportions of different vegetation types are shown in Table 4. These results indicate the overall frequency of distribution and occurrence of vegetation between sites, but cannot be used to calculate precise areas covered by each moorland vegetation type. This is because records relate only to presence or absence within each quadrat.

A number of plant communities are clearly dominant on the hills. The two dwarf shrub heath communities B1a and B1b occur in 16% and 19% of squares respectively and tended to occur in drier conditions and on valley sides and more strongly sloped areas.

Agrostis-Festuca grasslands (C1) and *Nardus stricta* grasslands (C2) occur in 70% and 47% of squares respectively. The widespread occurrence of these acid grasslands indicate a long history of grazing management, which have perhaps reduced *Calluna*-dominated vegetation and encouraged the spread of upland sheepwalk.

Blanket bog vegetation occurs not infrequently on most sites. Typical *Calluna-Eriophorum* mire and *Vaccinium* rich *Calluna-Eriophorum* mire occur in 26% and 10% of squares, whilst relative abundance of *Eriophorum*-dominated mire, which is generally species-poor, is again indicative of a history of overgrazing and over-burning.

Flush vegetation such as *Juncus effusus-Sphagnum recurvum* mire (H2a) occurs in 29% of the squares. However, the absolute area covered by this vegetation is undoubtedly lower than this high occurrence value might suggest, since it tends to occur in narrow linear belts alongside streams and other watercourses.

EROSIAN RECORDING

Table 5 records the frequency of erosion at each site. This is shown in terms of the number of 4ha squares containing each erosion category. Sites differed appreciably in the degree to which they showed peatland erosion. Generally, however, they were not highly eroded, which was in contrast to areas such as Shetland and the Isle of Lewis (NCC unpublished). Sites such as Earl's Seat (K1) and Hart Hill (K2) showed much more evidence of erosion than other sites such as Earl's Hill (K7) and Fintry Hills (K5).

HABITAT USE BY CURLEWS AND GOLDEN PLOVERS

Use and selection of moorland habitat by birds is complex and affected by a great variety of factors (Haworth 1987). In this survey Golden Plovers were noted to prefer areas with short vegetation that occurred either as a result of altitude (stunted, wind-blown vegetation) or recently burnt areas among heather moorlands. Curlews were noted to prefer *Juncus* flushes or areas of tall, wet vegetation. However, birds also respond to topography. An analysis was undertaken to see if consistent topographic selection occurred which might allow prediction of bird use in unsurveyed areas based solely on information on slope, aspect and altitude. Such information is an important first step in the development of more complex selection models taking into account a greater variety of habitat features including vegetation.

The present study, described in detail by Harding *et al.* (1988) compared the distribution of a large number of evenly spaced points on sites K1-K8 with the distribution of all sightings of Golden Plovers and Curlews on the same sites. This method can be used to investigate habitat preferences without having to map areas of land with the similar slope, altitude or aspect (Marcum and Loftsgaarden 1980). For those sites visited five times, only data from the first four visits were used to ensure comparability. The analysis uses the total number of sightings as an indication of use of different habitats by breeding birds. Easterbee and Pitkin (1984) showed that for sites in southern Scotland and northern England, the total number of sightings was directly proportional to the estimated minimum number of breeding pairs.

If the number of registrations falling within a habitat category is divided by the number of evenly spaced points falling within the same habitat category an index of density is obtained. This can be used to identify differences in density between habitat types. However, caution is necessary in interpreting such figures as purely by chance one would expect some variation in density between habitat types. There is thus a need to separate genuine trends from random variation. The approach adopted was to look for trends which were consistent across sites. The more sites a given trend is observed on, the less likely is the possibility that the trend is not genuine and is due purely to chance (Harding *et al.* 1988). In Tables 6 and 7, where the lack of evenly spaced points suggests that no habitat fell within a given category, asterisks are placed in the appropriate entry.

Altitude

Results for habitat use with respect to altitude by Curlew are presented in Table 6. Within most sites there was a tendency for the density index to decline with increasing altitude. Also, the highest density indices are recorded on the lowest sites (K4, K6, K7, K8), indicating that Curlew densities appear to decline with increasing altitude. No Golden Plovers occurred below 350m and at only one site did they occur below 400m. However, the data are too scanty to detect any trends in density within the altitudinal range where sightings occurred. Golden Plover densities are highest at high altitudes.

Slope

Curlews occur at very low densities on slopes steeper than 30% (Table 7). However, on slopes of less than 30% there is no trend of density with slope which is consistent across sites. No Golden Plovers were recorded on slopes steeper than 30%. In four out of six sites where Golden Plovers occurred, the highest densities were recorded for slopes less than 5%, although for K1 this result was a tie. For the remaining two sites the highest densities occurred on slopes of less than 10%. Golden Plover densities were highest on gentle slopes.

Aspect

There was no consistent relationship, across all sites, between Curlew or Golden Plover densities and aspect. For both species, and for each of the habitat variables examined, there was large variation between sites within any one habitat category. This suggests that each of the variables examined only explains a small part of the variation observed in the density index. Clearly habitat selection is complex and ideally the effects of different habitat features need to be investigated together rather than in isolation.

Discussion

In this study Golden Plovers were found to prefer higher, gently sloping ground. The results suggest that Curlews are more tolerant of steeper slopes than Golden Plovers. This may be an artefact since for Curlews most registrations were of flying birds, whereas for Golden Plovers most registrations were of birds on the ground. So, for Curlews most registrations are likely to occur in or over non-breeding habitat than for Golden Plovers. This would give the impression that they were more catholic in their tastes than Golden Plovers. Ratcliffe (1976) suggested that throughout Britain the highest breeding densities of Golden Plovers occurred at moderate elevations of 305 to 610m. Haworth (1986) found for a 150km^2 study area in the southern Pennines that the preference of Golden Plover for nesting in an area was stronger the greater the proportion of land above 427m. Both of these results are consistent with the absence of Golden Plovers at lower altitudes in the Campsies area. Ratcliffe (1976) suggested that Golden Plovers will not breed on slopes greater than around 11%, whilst the majority of the Golden Plovers in Haworth's study area preferred slopes of not more than 6%. These figures are very similar to those associated with the present study. Haworth (1986) found that in the southern Pennines, though Curlews selected for higher ground within the study area, the majority occurred at lower altitudes than Golden Plovers. Curlews preferred gently sloping areas. These trends are the same as those observed in the Campsie Fells/Touch Hills area.

AREAS OF CONSERVATION IMPORTANCE

The conservation significance of survey sites have been discussed by Calladine *et al.* (1987). Although the survey did not indicate areas of major importance for breeding waders in a national or international context, there are clearly regionally significant populations. One area of importance is the north-west of the Campsies massif (including the Earls Seat, Hart Hill and Ballglass Corrie). This has some of the most undamaged blanket bog, and high relative numbers of Golden Plover, Dunlin and Twite. Another area of importance includes the grouse moors above Gargunnock which extend towards Earls Hill and the reservoirs in the west.

The implications of the topographic analysis is that hill-tops and plateau areas will hold more breeding waders than steep slopes. However, the steep slopes and crags are also of importance for a variety of other bird species such as Twite and Ring Ouzel. Quantifying the relationship between birds and topography (or other habitat variables) makes the formulation of practical guidelines for forestry and other land uses feasible.

ACKNOWLEDGEMENTS

We are particularly grateful to the landowners, farmers and gamekeepers who kindly gave permission for the survey to be undertaken, and for their help and advice during the survey. The survey was undertaken by SD and JC, supervised by Kevin Shepherd. Johnathon Turner and Kevin Shepherd analysed the survey maps. We are most grateful to Caroline Crawford and the NCC Stirling sub-office for their considerable help in organising the survey. Both Roger Broad, RSPB and John Mitchell, NCC gave help and advice concerning the selection of survey areas and discussion of the results.

The survey was financed by the Chief Scientist Directorate of the NCC (Project No. 433) as part of the continuing studies of moorland bird ecology throughout Britain.

REFERENCES

BIRKS, H. J. B. and RATCLIFFE, D. A. 1980. Upland vegetation types. A list of National Vegetation Classification plant communities. Unpublished NCC report.

CALLADINE, J., DOUGILL, S., SHEPHERD, K. B., STROUD, D. A., TURNER, J. and CRAWFORD, C. M. 1987. A survey of moorland birds on the Campsie Fells/Touch Hills massif, Stirling in 1987. NCC, Chief Scientist Directorate Report No. 767.

CAMPBELL, L. H. 1985. Habitat features as a means of identifying areas of importance for moorland breeding birds. In: Bird Census and Atlas Studies. Proceedings of the VIII International Conference on Bird Census and Atlas Work, edited by K. Taylor, R. J. Fuller and P. C. Lack. Pp.269-272. Tring, BTO.

GALBRAITH, H. 1987. Threats to breeding waders: the impact of changing agricultural land-use in the breeding ecology of Lapwings. *Wader Study Group Bulletin* 49, *Suppl./IWRB Special Publication* 7, 102-104.

GREEN, R. E. 1985. Estimating the abundance of breeding snipe. *Bird Study,* 32, 141-149.

HARDING, N., SHEPHERD, K. B., and STROUD, D. A. 1988. Moorlands of the Campsie Fells and Touch Hills: their use by breeding birds. NCC, Chief Scientist Directorate Report No. 800.

HAWORTH, P. 1986. Moorland management and nature conservation in the South Pennines. Unpublished PhD. thesis, Manchester Polytechnic. 274pp.

MARCUM, C. L., and LOFTSGAARDEN, D. O. 1980. A non-mapping technique for studying habitat preferences. *Journal of Wildlife Management,* 44, 963-968.

MITCHELL, J., and BROAD, R. A. 1987. Close nesting of Peregrines in Stirlingshire. *The Glasgow Naturalist,* 21, 359.

RATCLIFFE, D. A. 1976. Observations on the breeding of the Golden Plover in Great Britain. *Bird Study,* 23, 63-116.

REED, T. M. 1982. Transect Methods. Unpublished NCC report.

REED, T M. 1985. Grouse moors and wading birds. *Game Conservancy Annual Report,* 16, 57-60.

REED, T. M., and LANGSLOW, D. R. 1985. The timing of breeding in the Golden Plover *Pluvialis apricaria.* As Campbell, L. H. above pp.123-9.

SMITH, K. W. 1981. Snipe censusing methods. *Bird Study,* 28, 246-248.

STROUD, D. A., REED, T. M., PIENKOWSKI, M. W. and LINDSAY, R. A. 1987. Birds, Bogs and Forestry: the Peatlands of Caithness and Sutherland. NCC, Peterborough, 219pp.

THOM, V. 1986. Birds in Scotland. Poyser, Calton. 382pp.

Editor's Note
All comment/correspondence about this paper should be addressed to D. A. Stroud, not Calladine, Dougill or Harding.

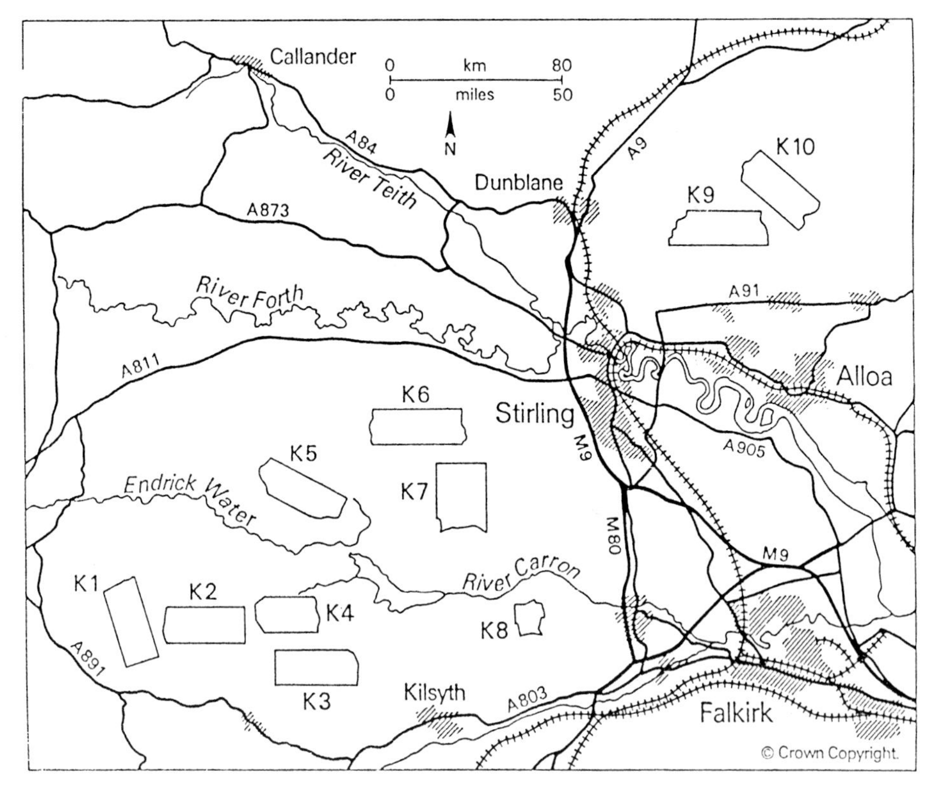

Location map showing distribution of study sites—by Stewart Wallace.

Table 1. Details of locations and areas of survey sites.

Site Name	Code	Area (ha)	Grid Ref.	Altitude range (m above sea level)
Earls Seat	K1	536	ND5682	310-578
Hart Hill	K2	578	NS6082	395-551
Cort-ma-law	K3	667	NS6580	395-547
Campsie Muir	K4	474	NS6583	260-460
Fintry Hills	K5	602	NS6490	315-511
Gargunnock	K6	707	NS6891	245-485
Earls Hill	K7	687	NS7288	270-441
Darrach Hill	K8	178	NS7582	240-351
Menstrie Moss	K9	671	NN8600	290-565
Alva Moss	K10	618	NN8801	390-705

Table 3. Minimum breeding densities (pairs/km^2) of commoner waders and Wheatear on sites in Campsie Fells and west Ochil Hills area, 1987.

Site	Golden Plover	Lapwing	Snipe	Curlew	Wheatear
K1	0.74		0.19	1.12	0.37
K2	0.87			3.11	0.17
K3	0.45			1.35	0.30
K4		0.42	0.21	2.74	0.84
K5	0.33			0.66	
K6	0.28	0.15		0.99	0.14
K7	0.44	0.30	0.29	2.33	0.44
K8		0.56	0.56	3.37	1.69
K9	0.30		0.45	1.34	0.74
K10	1.46		0.32	0.65	0.48

Table 2. Minimum numbers of pairs of breeding birds found on survey sites in the Campsie Fells and west Ochil Hills areas in 1987.

Site name	Earls Seat	Hart Hill	Cort-ma-law	Campsie Muir	Fintry Hills	Gar-gunnock	Earls Hill	Darrach Hill	Menstrie Moss	Alva Moss
Code	K1	K2	K3	K4	K5	K6	K7	K8	K9	K10
No. of visits	4	5	5	5	4	4	5	5	5	5
Grey heron			+	+						
Teal										+
Mallard	+	+	+			+	+	+	+	+
Hen harrier	+									
Sparrowhawk							+			
Buzzard		+								+
Kestrel	+		+			+	+			+
Peregrine		+				+				
Red grouse	L	H	L	L	L	L	H	H	L	L
Black grouse	+		+	+	+		+		+	
Grey partridge									+	
Peasant					+					
Golden plover	4	5	3		2	2	3		2	9
Lapwing				2		1	2	1	+	
Dunlin		2	1							
Jack snipe										+
Snipe	1				1		2	1	3	2
Curlew	6	18	9	13	4	7	16	6	9	4
Common sandpiper				1		1				
Black-headed gull						12				
Lesser black-backed gull			+				+			
Herring gull			+							
Cuckoo									+	
Short-eared owl		+	+			+	+			
Skylark	*	*	*	*	*	*	*	*	*	*
Meadow pipit	*	*	*	*	*	*	*	*	*	*
Grey wagtail	+			+						
Dipper	1			+	+	+	+			1
Wren						1				
Whinchat			+	+		4	+		1	
Wheatear	2	1	2	4		1	3	3	5	3
Carrion crow		1			+	+				
Raven	+	+			+				+	+
Chaffinch				1		+	+			
Linnet								+		
Twite						+				1
No. of species breeding	8	8	7	10	5	11	9	7	8	9

Key
L Breeding in relatively low densities
H Breeding in relatively high densities
* Breeding in unknown numbers
+ Present, no proof of breeding

Table 4. Frequency of 200m x 200m 'quadrats' on each site containing differing upland plant communities after Birks & Ratcliffe (1980). Note that more than one plant community occurs within each quadrat, such that totals and proportions are not additive. Percentage figures indicate the proportion of total number of quadrats containing a particular plant community.

Total quadrats per site	K1	K2	K3	K4	K5	K6	K7	K8	Total	
	132	138	155	113	137	169	165	31	1040	
Bla	7				8	86	62	8	171	16.4%
Blb						73	103	19	195	18.7%
B2								1	1	0.1%
B3		11					4	15	30	2.9%
C1	91	49	94	113	116	124	120	24	731	70.3%
C2	86	6	10	61	115	93	103	19	493	47.4%
C3					6				6	0.6%
C5a						34			34	3.3%
D7						19	3		22	2.1%
G1a							6		6	0.6%
G2a							5		5	0.5%
G4a	71	57		7	30	61	40		266	25.6%
G4e	8	70	9				21		108	10.4%
G4f	26	43	122		52				243	23.4%
H2a	3	14	13	86	22	52	94	22	306	29.4%
H2b								15	15	1.4%
H2c								3	3	0.3%
H3		10		2		10	24	1	47	4.5%
H3c			4						4	0.4%
J4						6			6	0.6%
M3		1							1	0.1%

Key
B. DWARF SHRUB HEATHS
B1a *Calluna* dry heath
B1b *Calluna-Sphagnum* damp heath
B2 Montane (prostrate) *Calluna vulgaris* heath
B3 *Vaccinium myrtillus-Empetrum nigrum/hermaphroditum* heath
C. UPLAND GRASSLANDS
C1 *Agrostis-Festuca* grassland
C2 *Nardus stricta* grassland
C3 *Juncus squarrosus* grassland
C5a Species poor *Deschampsia caespitosa* grassland
G. BLANKET BOGS (ombrogenous mires)
G1a *Sphagnum*-rich *Tricophorum-Myrica* mire
G2a *Sphagnum*-rich *Tricophorum-Calluna* mire
G4a Typical *Calluna-Eriophorum* mire
G4e *Vaccinium*-rich *Calluna-Eriophorum* mire
G4f *Eriophorum*-dominated mire
H. FLUSH BOGS AND FENS (soligenous and topogenous mires)
H2a *Juncus effusus-Sphagnum recurvum* mire
H2b *Juncus acutiflorus-Sphagnum recurvum* mire
H2c *Juncus acutiflorus* herb-brown moss mire
H3 *Carex*-moss mire
H3c *Carex rostrata-Sphagnum recurvum* mire

Table 5. Number of 4 ha squares containing different degrees of peatland erosion. 0 = no erosion, 1 = micro-erosion, 2 = slight erosion, 3 = moderate erosion, 4 = severe erosion, 5 = more or less complete loss of peat.

EROSION CATEGORIES

	0	1	2	3	4	5
K1	**95**	**79**	**43**	**13**	**2**	**0**
K2	**62**	**86**	**58**	**13**	**5**	**0**
K3	**120**	**86**	**41**	**1**	**0**	**0**
K4	**106**	**27**	**7**	**0**	**0**	**0**
K5	**129**	**19**	**6**	**0**	**0**	**0**
K6	**154**	**38**	**17**	**5**	**0**	**0**
K7	**161**	**14**	**0**	**0**	**0**	**0**
K8	**31**	**0**	**0**	**0**	**0**	**0**
TOTALS	**858**	**349**	**172**	**32**	**7**	**0**
	60.5%	**24.6%**	**12.1%**	**2.2%**	**0.5%**	**0%**

KEY

0. *No surface erosion.* High water-tables and extensive ground cover of vegetation with no areas of bare peat either on the surface or along pool edges.
1. *'Micro-erosion'.* Very slight erosion in some places. Perceptable lowering of water-tables with some bare peat exposed on edges of pools. Generally less than 5% of total area affected.
2. *Slight erosion.* Beginnings of gully erosion on slopes. Where peat-banks are present, these show signs of active wind or sheep erosion. Usually less than half total area is affected. Ground is noticably dry underfoot. Gullies, where present, are less than 12″ deep.
3. *Moderate erosion.* Gullies are 1 – 3′ deep. Few remaining aquatic or wringing wet plant communities due to lowering of the water-table. There is notably active movement of peat by wind/rain in some areas, although few areas are totally devegetated however.
4. *Severe erosion.* Deep gullies more than 3′ deep. Characterised by major loss of surface vegetation in some areas and essentially no aquatic or *Sphagnum* communities. Much movement of particulate peat.
5. *More or less complete loss of peat.* Either loss of peat revealing underlying drift/bedrock or extensive areas of unvegetated bare peat. Characterised by almost no moorland vegetation and no pools or natural aquatic zones.

Table 6. Selection Indices for Curlew and Golden Plover with respect to altitude (m above sea level). Values >1 indicate active selection, values = 1 indicates no selection, values <1 indicate active avoidance.

CURLEW

	SITE								
Altitude range	K1	K2	K3	K4	K5	K6	K7	K8	Total
250 – 300	****	****	****	3.14	****	3.25	3.20	1.80	2.92
300 – 350	****	****	****	4.18	****	2.29	2.24	2.14	2.76
350 – 400	1.00	****	****	3.56	2.00	0.50	1.46	****	1.94
400 – 450	1.00	2.00	1.33	1.00	0.26	0.10	0.88	****	0.53
450 – 500	1.18	1.74	1.45	****	0.09	0.00	****	****	1.16
500 – 550	0.50	0.60	0.93	****	2.00	****	****	****	0.76
550 – 600	0.00	1.00	****	****	****	****	****	****	0.50

GOLDEN PLOVER

	SITE								
Altitude range	K1	K2	K3	K4	K5	K6	K7	K8	Total
250 – 300	****	****	****	0.00	****	0.00	0.00	0.00	0.00
300 – 350	****	****	****	0.00	****	0.00	0.00	0.00	0.00
350 – 400	0.00	****	****	0.00	0.00	0.00	0.31	****	0.12
400 – 450	0.17	0.00	0.17	0.00	0.09	0.10	1.00	****	0.21
450 – 500	0.06	0.26	0.00	****	0.18	0.00	****	****	0.11
500 – 550	1.13	0.40	0.21	****	0.00	****	****	****	0.48
550 – 600	0.00	0.00	****	****	****	****	****	****	0.00

Table 7. Selection Indices for Curlew and Golden Plover with respect to slope (degrees). Indices as in Table 6.

CURLEW

	SITE								
Slope range	K1	K2	K3	K4	K5	K6	K7	K8	Total
0 - 5	0.60	1.00	2.00	0.67	0.20	0.50	1.88	****	1.02
5 - 10	0.80	2.08	1.40	2.75	0.33	1.23	2.00	4.00	1.44
10 - 15	1.00	0.62	1.36	4.23	0.71	0.78	1.94	1.43	1.57
15 - 20	3.00	0.67	0.00	1.67	0.50	0.00	5.00	3.00	1.26
20 - 25	2.00	****	1.75	****	1.33	0.00	1.00	****	2.35
25 - 30	****	****	****	****	****	****	****	****	****
30 - 35	0.25	****	0.00	****	0.00	0.00	****	0.33	0.70
35 - 40	****	****	****	****	****	****	****	****	****
40 - 45	****	****	****	****	****	****	****	****	****
45 - 50	1.00	****	0.00	****	****	****	****	****	2.00

GOLDEN PLOVER

	SITE								
Slope range	K1	K2	K3	K4	K5	K6	K7	K8	Total
0 - 5	1.00	0.57	0.50	0.00	0.60	0.00	0.13	****	0.38
5 - 10	0.10	0.46	0.07	0.00	0.00	0.15	0.35	0.00	0.17
10 - 15	0.25	0.00	0.00	0.00	0.14	0.00	0.19	0.00	0.06
15 - 20	1.00	0.00	0.25	0.00	0.00	0.00	0.00	0.00	0.11
20 - 25	0.67	****	0.00	****	0.00	0.00	0.33	****	0.18
25 - 30	****	****	****	****	****	****	****	****	****
30 - 35	0.00	****	0.00	****	0.00	0.00	****	0.00	0.00
35 - 40	****	****	****	****	****	****	****	****	****
40 - 45	****	****	****	****	****	****	****	****	****
45 - 50	0.00	****	0.00	****	****	****	****	****	0.00

BOOK REVIEWS

DRYMEN AND BUCHANAN — In Old Photographs. Mary Bruce and Alison Brown. Stirling District Libraries. 1988. 48pp. ISBN 1 870542 11 8. £2.50.

This small collection of photographs ranging from 1873 to the 1930s, with one rather oddly of the football club of 1956/7, offers an interesting and varied insight into changes and continuities in Drymen and the surrounding area. Photographs have been well chosen showing buildings and people, work and leisure, rich and poor, village, farm and country house. The captions are kept sufficiently brief not to intrude in what is essentially a visual book, while at the same time stimulating interest. The quality of printing is good, always a problem with old photographs. Anyone interested in Drymen will be encouraged by the prefacing remark that the Local History Society have established a photographic collection. Such valuable preservation work complements publication and is to be commended as is this book. It is a resource for the community, for the local historian and for the teachers and pupils in our schools.

D. Murphy

PATTERNS OF ERROR: The Teacher and External Authority, 1581-1861. Andrew Bain. 228pp. 1989.

This is a comprehensive survey of the major offences of teachers over a period of three hundred years in the former counties of West Lothian, Stirlingshire, Clackmannanshire, Fife, and Kinross. It not only provides a historical explanation where this is appropriate (for example, in relation to witchcraft, the 1715 and 1745 rebellions, and the Disruption), but also analyses the rich diversity of human response and weakness that can be found in any age.

Some received ideas about the attitude and procedures of the churches in relation to offenders in this social group would appear to require some modification.

The book (paperback) published privately for the author by Moubray House may be purchased direct from the author at 22 Clarendon Road, Linlithgow, price £10 plus £1 p&p.

L. Corbett

THE SPRING RETURN OF MOORLAND BIRDS TO THE OCHIL HILLS OF CENTRAL SCOTLAND

C. J. Henty

Upland moorlands such as those on the Ochil Hils, Central Region, characteristically have considerable breeding populations of waders and small passerines that are largely or entirely absent during winter. Thus in spring there is the notable and welcome return of these species to the uplands. Although these events are well known and the first recorded dates of return are regularly reported, there are few studies in which the whole sequence is followed up to the point where the full breeding population is established.

The lower western slopes of the Ochils support abundant populations of Curlew (*Numenius arquata*), Skylark (*Alauda arvensis*) and Meadow Pipit (*Anthus pratensis*), as well as smaller numbers of other species, so I decided to try and study the spring return by making a series of transect counts throughout the spring. Two main questions were set up in advance—

1) Are there species differences in the time pattern of arrival of the breeding populations?

2) Does the return of any particular species involve a steady and fairly slow increase or can one or more mass influxes be detected?

STUDY AREA AND METHODS

The study area covered two of the major moorland types and a smaller area around a deserted farmstead. The first moorland area, hereafter called the 'low moor' (a 3.4km liner transect) is between 180 and 230m altitude with mixed patches of Heather *Calluna vulgaris* and rough grass; it is regularly burnt. The topography is irregular and includes several drainage ditches and boggy areas. The second moorland area, the 'high moor' (a 3.6 km transect), extends from 206 to 415m, mainly above 260m and with extensive steep slopes, and is almost totally covered in rough grass; there are a few rocky outcrops, small burns, boggy patches with rushes *Juncus sp* and some small areas of Bracken *Pteridium aquilinum*. The final area (a 1.6 km transect) lies between the low and high moors and is about half pasture and half an almost bare and heavily trampled field that had a root crop for sheep fodder, grown the previous year. This third section is crossed by two medium sized burns, one of which is in a deep gully with a dense growth of bushes and small trees. The whole area is heavily grazed by sheep and was chosen to provide a manageable transect that covered the major habitat types of the lower and medium altitude moors; it was not feasible to design a route that included the highest peat mosses or ridges.

The general plan was to make repeated transects (about weekly) in the early spring (March and early April) and the more at longer intervals until it seemed certain that the full breeding population had returned. Transect counts were made in the morning and only on days with good conditions for observation, i.e. with wind less than force four, no mist and no rain except possibly for brief showers. My method was to walk steadily over the area recording small birds up to about 100m away and larger species up to 200m. These distances correspond roughly to the distances at which it was easy to detect birds with the naked eye, no attempt was made to scan systemically with binoculars either at random or to sight singing but invisible individuals. Each record had to be of a bird positively identified and seen, irrespective of how it might have been detected initially, and with reasonable certainty that it was not an individual already noted. In the rare case where I was uncertain whether a record was either a new individual or within the standard distance then I noted it as a "half chance" and added a record for that species if an additional "half chance" occurred later. In fact the data would be similar if a different criterion had been used for borderline cases.

I followed the same transect line for each count, except for small variations due to the difficulties of precise route finding in irregular and featureless terrain or where detours had to be made to avoid disturbing flocks of sheep. For other practical reasons the start and end of the transect were interchanged during the study.

RESULTS

The number of Curlew, Skylarks and Meadow Pipit recorded over the whole area are shown in Figure 1 together with the combined total of large resident species (game birds, pigeons, Kestrel *Falco tinnunculus* and Carrion Crow *Corvus corone*) that can act as a rough check for variations in conditions of observation. The numbers of the last group of resident species do not increase during the course of the study.

The data are further summarised in Table 1 which shows the dates of two stages of return for the whole area and separately for the low moor and the high moor. Two stages were considered –

a) Primary arrival, when numbers first equalled 20% of final asymptote.
b) Major arrival, when numbers first equalled 60% of final asymptote.

Since occasional individuals can appear at almost any time, the date of the very first record is unreliable; however, Figure 1 shows that sometime after mid-March the recorded numbers start to fluctuate around a rough plateau representing the complete breeding population — hence an average figure for this asymptote can be calculated. Figure 1 also suggests that in several cases there is an initial distinct small arrival followed by a later rise to the asymptote and the figures of 20% and 60% were taken to represent these two, the primary and the major arrivals. I am aware that a 50% criterion has been used for Willow Warblers

(*Phylloscopus trochilus*) by Lawn (1980) but in that study the main interest was in comparing the best estimate for spring arrival betwen two sets of years. In addition Lawn's arrival curves were fairly smooth so that a single measure is quite adequate, this is not true of my data.

Figure 1: Spring returns to moors

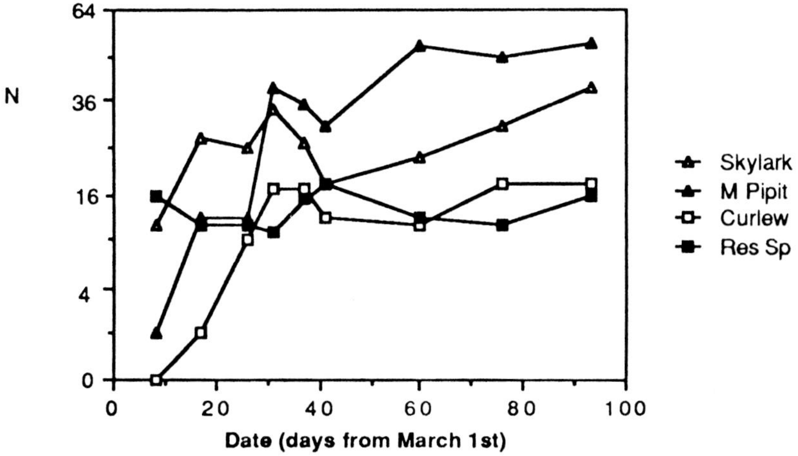

N is number of records for the 8.6 km of transects (on a square root scale)

Skylarks were already present in numbers (primary arrival) on the first transect of March 8, though none were present on February 15 during a visit to the general area of the low moor when there was a complete snow cover. Numbers reached plateau level by March 17 so tht on these data Skylarks might either have returned in two major influxes or there could have been a fairly rapid but steady return over a week or so in early to mid-March. There was no dramatic difference in times of return to the low versus high moors except that the major arrival on the high moor was delayed by one visit (9 days).

Table 1 Dates in March 1986 of Primary and Major Arrivals

PA=Primary Arrival. MA=Major Arrival

	Whole area		Low moor		High moor	
	PA	MA	PA	MA	PA	MA
Skylark	8	17	8	17	8	26
Meadow Pipit	17	31	17	31	26	31
Curlew	26	26	26	26	26	31

NB: An actual influx must have occurred between the date specified and the date of the previous count; for Skylarks the primary arrival had already occurred at the time of the first count.

Meadow Pipits returned later than Skylarks and it is worth noting that the primary arrival of March 17 was largely composed of one small flock, the pipits were not generally dispersed until March 26. The data show at least one other influx between March 26 and 31 and possibly some birds coming in between April 10 and 29. However the number for the low moor on April 10 was exceptionally small and I suspect some artefact since the same effect was noted for Skylarks, although both species were in stable numbers on the high moor; possibly birds on the low moor were affected by some predator. The primary arrival of pipits was about nine days earlier to the low moor but the major arrival is the same date, March 31, on both low and high moors.

Wheaters (*Oenanthe oenanthe*) and Whinchats (*Saxicola rubetra*), the two trans-Saharan migrants, arrived later. Numbers are two small to use the quantitative criteria, however the first records were April 6 for Wheatear and May 16 for Whinchat.

The primary arrival of Curlew was on March 26 which was also the date of major arrival for the whole area, there is a suggestion that major arrival on the high moor was later but the figures are too small and variable to be relied on. Lapwings (*Vanellus vanellus*) were restriced to small numbers around the farmstead, after a single bird on March 17 the bulk of the population was present on March 26. A few Snipe (*Capella gallinago*) were noted on the low moor whilst a pair of Oystercatchers (*Haematopus ostralegus*) appeared on the pasture only on May 16 although the species was on nearby lowland farmland for many weeks before this.

To give an idea of the final level of abundance Table 2 shows for the

Table 2 Mean asymptotic numbers of birds per km of transect.

	Whole area	Low Moor	High Moor
Skylark	3.5	3.6	3.9
Meadow Pipit	5.4	6.9	5.5
Curlew	2.1	2.5	1.7

NB: Records of Curlew were taken up to 200m from observer, other species up to 100m.

three commonest species the mean asymptotic number per kilometre of transect for the whole area and the low and high moors. Meadow Pipits are clearly more frequently recorded than Skylarks in the final breeding population ($p<0.002$, 2 tailed t test) but for both there is little difference between low and high moors. Curlew seem to be more frequent on the low moor but the difference is not quite significant statistically (2 tailed t test on the last 6 transects).

DISCUSSION

The straigtforward interpretation, given above, of the basic data does depend on two main assumptions – that there is little through passage and that the counts are not often markedly affected by random effects on observability.

Through passage can in principle be detected either by direct observation of visible migration or by the occurrence of marked peak counts before the plateau period. Visible migration of larks and pipits is frequently seen in this area in autumn but I have never seen any indications in spring. Similarly, the total area counts in Figure 1 show no evidence of the temporary presence of passage birds although daily counts would ideally be needed to explore this possibility thoroughly. At least there is no reason to suppose that through passage is upsetting the main conclusions of the study.

The only marked erratic variation in counts applies to several counts of larks and pipits on the low moor in April, these are puzzling and not explicable by bad weather or observation conditions. However, since these occurred after the main arrival over the whole area they do not effect the conclusions.

It is course true that a mapping method can give more reliable results for a stable population and can be interpreted in terms of density per square kilometre. It would, however, be quite impractical to monitor a changing population by mapping over any area large enough to give representative results whilst, following Verner (1986), the questions posed here are logically answerable by a method using relative frequencies. The main problem would be if there were marked variations in detectability from one day to another. The restriction of transects to days when observation conditions were fairly good was intended to minimise variations due to weather. Since song frequency might vary through the course of the study I made notes on the frequency of song on a subjective scale (occasional, regular, sustained), no obvious relation was found between this and the recorded numbers of birds. The technique of noting birds only within a restricted distance would reduce any gross effect of song on detection, about only a third of the individuals seen were noted solely during song flights. In comparing species it is important to bear in mind their relative detectabilities. In Finnish woodlands for example, Hilden and Laine (1985) note that Willow Warblers (*Phylloscopus trochilus*) were over twice as conspicuous as Willow Tits (*Parus montanus*). They also note however, that these results accord well with general experience. Hence I judge that the relative frequencies of Skylarks and Meadow Pipits in the present study are fairly reliable, certainly there is no reason to doubt that the pipits are in fact the commoner species.

The fact that counts were not done daily does mean that I could have missed brief desertions of the moors due to severe weather. There are strong indications that this may happen since Meadow Pipits may appear in flocks away from the breeding areas during cold spells in April, e.g. I saw 70 on the lawns of Stirling University on 8th April 1975 when there was snow on the hills. There was in fact wintry weather in mid April 1986 with the snow line at c300m on the 17th, unfortunately I was unable to make transects during this period.

The spring of 1986 was noticeably cold and late so it should not be assumed that the pattern of spring arrival detailed in this study applies in all years. I can, however, use temperature data from the Carim Lodge meteorological station operated by the Department of Environmental Science, University of Stirling, to say a little more about temperature and bird numbers. The station is at an altitude of c325m, GR NN 864049, and some 6.5 km NE of my study area. I have calculated the average of the daily mean temperatures for the periods between counts, or for five day periods before a count if the interval between counts was longer. In early March the average daily temperature was only 0.3°C but rose to nearly 4.0 before the primary influx of Meadow Pipits. There was then a spell of cold weather until April 20 with daily temperatures usually below 1.5°C but during the middle of this period there were major arrivals of Meadow Pipits and Curlews. In late April daily temperatures rose rapidly to reach a plateau of around 7°C through May. This suggests that, in the establishment of birds on the breeding moors, a major factor might be the absence of successive days with continuous frost rather than the achieving of temperatures typical of mid-April.

In conclusion I think that the spring arrival pattern is clearly more complex and interesting than is indicated by the simple date of first appearance and that spaced transects can start to give some insight into the problem. It would be particularly interesting if studies in the future could cover habitats with a greater range in altitude.

REFERENCES

HILDEN, O. and LAINE, L.J., 1985. Accuracy of single line transects in Finnish woodland habitat, pp 111-116 K. Taylor, R. J. Fuller and P. C. Lack (Editors), Bird Census and Atlas Studies: Proceedings VII International Conference on Bird Census and Atlas Work. BTO, Tring.

LAWN, M.R., 1980. Late arrival of Willow Warblers in recent years. *British Birds* 73, 357-358.

IN SEARCH OF THE BUCHANAN FERN II

John Mitchell

In an earlier paper (*Forth Naturalist and Historian* 6, 97-100A) my co-author and I described the 19th century discovery, propagation and subsquent search for surviving examples of Stirlingshire's most noteworthy fern — *Athyrium filix-femina* 'Victoriae,' better known locally as the Buchanan fern. Our quest was not without success, for several examples of this particularly fine variety of Lady Fern were found in three private gardens in and around Drymen. However, although more or less perfect in form and symmetry (see first paper for description and photograph), all the ferns examined had fronds lacking the height and rigidity of the original specimen which once graced the grounds of Buchanan Castle. It was suspected therefore that these were probably all 'progeny' (second or later generations grown from spores), rather than root-stock divisions of the parent plant. We concluded with the thought that somewhere in the district a direct descendant of the original Buchanan Fern possibly still survived. Then just as it seemed the trail had gone cold, our optimism was rewarded.

But first, an update on the background to the Buchanan Fern presented in the first account. James Cosh, who found this quite unique plant growing wild in 1861, has always appeared a rather shadowy figure. Over the years all writers on the subject could give only his name and that at the time of the discovery he was a young man studying in Edinburgh. Recently however, while rumaging through the archives of the Natural History Society of Glasgow, I unexpectedly came across Master Cosh's name again. In a manuscript paper on the distribution of ferns in the vicinity of Glasgow, a number of localities around the south-east corner of Loch Lomond are credited to one James Cosh of Drymen. Census returns of the period confirmed that Cosh had indeed been a local man. From the 1851 returns for the parish of Buchanan it was possible to ascertain that he must have been about ten years old when his family moved into the area ca.1849, James Cosh snr. having taken up employment as a carpenter on the Duke of Montrose's estate. They made their home at Gartlick (an almost forgotten name for a row of estate workers' cottages) alongside Buchanan Smithy, significantly only half-a-mile distant from Angle Plantation where the fern was later discovered. James Cosh jnr. does not appear in the census returns for 1861, presumably by then having moved to Edinburgh to pursue his academic studies.

Any botanical or horticultural historian now wishing to examine the walled garden and adjoining stone-built fernery at the castle, where the Buchanan Fern was formerly displayed, is in for a disappointment. During the mid-1980s this part of the grounds was redeveloped as an up-market housing estate, appropriately named 'Castle Gardens.' Several years before the overgrown fernery was destroyed however, a close search by the author showed nothing more unusual remaining than Ostrich Feather Fern *Matteuccia struthiopteris* and several huge, but moribund root-stocks of Royal Fern *Osmunda regalis*.

In August 1984 word was received that a well established clump of Buchanan Fern had been spotted in a garden at Boquhan, situated between the villages of Killearn and Balfron. This sounded promising, particularly as the garden owner's father had been employed on the Duke of Montrose's estate as a dry-stone waller. As such, his duties would not only have brought him into frequent contact with the Head Gardener at the castle, but given ready access to the walled garden and fernery. Visiting Boquhan on 20th August I was impressed with the carefully tended specimen from the start. With firm fronds up to 115cm in length growing from well over a dozen crowns, the fern presented a striking display. If there was any doubt at all of this being a direct descendant of the very plant which captured the fern-growing world's imagination nearly 125 years earlier, then it lay in only partial secondary crossing of the pinnules (the smallest leaflets), but this may not have been a consistent character even in the original.

Through the generosity of Mr G. Goodwin, portions of root-stock from the Boquhan specimen have been made available to the British Pteridological Society and to the gardens of Ross Priory on Loch Lomondside. It is to be hoped this measure will ensure a continuing future for the Scottish 'Queen amongst Lady Ferns.'

REFERENCES

ANON. 1863. List of Localities for Ferns around Glasgow and its Watering Places. *The Manuscript Magazine of the Glasgow Naturalists Society* 4:158-168.

MITCHELL, J and MASON, J.B. 1981. In search of the Buchanan Fern. *The Forth Naturalist and Historian* 6, 97-100A.

SOME EARLY GRAVESTONES IN THE HOLY RUDE KIRKYARD, STIRLING

John G. Harrison

SUMMARY

During the 16th and 17th centuries inscribed graveyard monuments became increasingly popular in Scotland, but they were still the prerogative of the few. The earliest were similar to the stones the elite set over burials in the kirks but later the headstone appeared; it was cheaper, more versatile and brought new groups into the market.

This paper looks at the emergence of graveyard stones, comparing the local documentary evidence with the stones themselves. I suggest that, since many of the stones in the Stirling area were put up before their owners' deaths, they should not be seen as memorials but as fashionable artefacts indicating ownership of the site and a new attitude to personality and family. The owners of these stones could visit them; the symbolism of life and death which they carry is not a message addressed by the dead to the living but an assertion by the owner of his own wealth and orthodoxy.

INTRODUCTION (1)

For a thousand years or so from late Roman times even the burials of the most wealthy and prestigious had been anonymous. It was better to be buried inside the church, close to the relics of the saints and near the High Altar, than to be buried outside; but the exact site did not matter and for centuries it was not marked, even for kings. From about the 12th century this began to change, at first only for the highest of the élites, later for a wider but still narrow spectrum of people who identified an area within the church as that where they would be buried, beside their ancestors. This site was marked, perhaps with an ornate tomb, increasingly often with a simple, inscribed slab.

By the 16th century Stirling's élite, together with the rural gentry of the locality, had marked burial sites within the kirk (2); but for the majority, who were probably buried in un-marked graves in the kirkyard, we have no information, either documentary or archaeological. During the 16th century inscribed outdoor stones began to appear with some regularity. The oldest surviving in Stirling is dated 1579. In 1628 the Stirling Kirk Session (3) decided that old kirkyard stones which had sunk into the ground should be raised, so that it could be known to whom they belonged; so clearly there were a number of inscribed stones by this time, some older than reliable memory.

These early stones closely resemble those which had covered graves in the kirk floor and like them were called thrughstanes. They are either flat slabs or have four sloping sides, rising to a central tablet (Plates 1 and 3 and Figure 1). The two types are usually now known as slabs and coped stones respectively.

The Session Minutes beginning in 1597 give an almost continuous record of policy and stone ownership till control of the graveyard was handed over to the municipal authorities in the 19th century. Minutes can be compared with the stones to identify initials, the only identification on many stones in the Stirling area. They tell not just the names of the applicants but their occupations and whether this is a traditional family plot or vacant ground. The bounds of the lair are given and the entry may tell us about adjacent stones. The Logie minutes for the late 17th and early 18th centuries indicate that in that parish it was common practice to set up two identical headstones at the same time and on the same lair; and many of these pairs can still be seen and identified (4).

Minutes confirm that many early stones have been lost, probably removed by later generations who wanted something more in keeping with newer fashions. It is probably for this reason that long abandoned churchyards like Logie and Kilmadock are such superb places for gravestone hunters (See 1, particularly Christison and RCAHMS). Minutes also give invaluable information about official policy and attitudes and about the concerns of the gravestone owners. When we find the Session arbitrating in disputes and developing well ordered procedures for avoiding them, we can be sure that it is because the disputes were bitter and involved deep feelings. Gravestones were important to people.

Officially, from the late 16th century, the kirk condemned burial in the kirk as 'desecration'; but it was prestigious, some families had particular rights to burial in private aisles and others were prepared to pay. On 25th February 1623 the Stirling Session expressed its ambiguous position. To avoid the 'great abuse and profanation of God, his house, in burying of dead corpses within the saids' they forbad all such burials for the future — unless a suitably large fee was paid. The cost of kirk burial varied. Under the tower (at the West end) it was quite cheap. But at the East end — where the old High Altar had once stood — it cost a massive 100 merks (£5.55 Sterling). The removal of the altar and relics had not diminished the prestige of this site. However, during the 17th and 18th centuries, the practice of church burial faded away, even for the elite. Those who wanted to set up stones in the kirkyard were not grand enough to meet the cost of kirk burial — and were perhaps too orthodox to face the disapproval of their neighbours.

In 1615 the Session noted that they received frequent petitions to set up stones in the kirkyard and expressed concern that too many stones would encroach on the limited space available; they agreed that anyone wishing to set up a stone could do so — but like kirk burial the practice was to be discouraged by charging a licence fee for the benefit of the poor. This Act has the air of attempting to formulate rules for a newish problem, something it had not been necessary to regulate before as it had been so infrequent. During the 17th century, as stones became more widespread, other Sessions in the locality also introduced licensing systems. In 1623 the executors of the late Robert Robertson were given permission to set up a stone over his corpse in the kirkyard, paying 20 merks in addition to the 40 he had already left in legacy. This is the first written record of a specific graveyard stone in Stirling. The total fee of 60 merks or £40 Scots is the same as the charge for burial at the West end of the kirk. In 1625, Andro Zoing and Andro Downy were given permission to set up stones 'bearing letters for their names', surely a reference to the use of initials for identification.

Probably all those old stones which the Session decided to raise in 1628 were either slabs or coped stones. But by 1640 they had been joined by a new type of stone, a radical departure in design. The Session noted that 'certain people, of their own hand, without licence' had set up

> 'little stones, one at the head and another at the food of the graves, some with their names engraven thereon.'

Very few footstones now survive anywhere; but the headstone was soon to become — and remain — the most popular type of gravestone in Scotland. The earliest recorded inscribed headstones in Scotland date from the 1620s (rather earlier than they appear in England) and are at Dunning, so Stirling was well up with the fashion. However, few 17th century examples now remain in the Holy Rude kirkyard; there are far more at Logie, where 'over 100' stones, mainly headstones, bear dates before 1707 (1e).

Headstones were less prestigious than thrughstanes; smaller size made them cheaper and the licence fee was about half that for a thrughstane. But the new style presented two — or more — surfaces for the mason to work on and the upright position helped to preserve them from wet and frost. Whilst thrughstanes continued to be set up by well established families, headstones belonged to less substantial people. But all stones were expensive and though headstones widened the market they were still confined to the few, in town to well known public figures such as magistrates and deacons of trades; in the country to the most prosperous artisans, substantial tenants and feuars who were increasing in both numbers and prosperity. Many of these people, whether rural or urban, whether or not they were organised into guilds and incorporations, had the symbols of their occupation cut on their stones in place of the shield or Coat of Arms so often found on thrughstanes.

Some stones were set up on traditional family burial plots, previously un-marked or with impermanent markers; or a family could buy a plot, a licence and a stone for it. Stone and plot were heritable family property;

they could even be sold — along with the contents of the grave! In 1648 the Session closed a dispute between two branches of the Blackburn family with a judgement of Solomon; if they continued to argue about ownership the Session would have the stone removed altogether! But in the Stirling area the applicant for the licence was rarely a grieving relative; more often it was a prosperous man, in the fullness of life (6). Stones were set up immediately the licence was granted — if not before. The main dates on the early stones are those of the licences. And in Logie, in November 1693, the Session supervised the setting up of some stones whilst their owners looked on.

THE STONES

The Sconce Monument

The largest monument in the Holy Rude kirkyard is this so-called Sconce Monument, close to the Back Walk on the South side (Mitchell No. 150). Other mural monuments in Stirling were demolished in 1857 (7) but a splendid and accurate painting by Mitchell in the Smith Art Gallery and Museum dated 1833 and a view of the kirkyard published in 1830 (8) show nothing else of comparable size.

Its architectural form is described in RCAHMS and I have written elsewhere about John McCulloch, founder of the Sconce dynasty, through the marriage of one of his daughters to John Sconce (9). However strange the sentiments of the text may be to modern taste, in their day they were as orthodox as skull, bones and sexton's spade. Its main inscription reads –

> HERE LIES THE CORPSE OF JOHN MCCULLOCH LEAT (sic) PROVOST OF STIRLING WHO DIED THE 5 OF OCTOBER 1689 YEARS OF AGE 54. REVELATIONS 14 VERSE 13. BLESED (sic) ARE THE DEAD WHO DIE IN THE LORD THAT THEY MAY REST FROM THEIR LABOURS AND THEIR WORKS DO FOLLOW THEM.
>
> ULTIMA SEMPER EXPECTANDA DIES HOMINI DICIQUE BEATUS ANTE OBITUM NEMO SUPREMAQUE FUNERA DEBET.
>
> (We must always await life's last day, and no one should be called happy until he is dead and buried.)

This is the most elaborate stone in the kirkyard; but extra cash was not used to extend the range of symbolism beyond the conventional or to tell us about John McCulloch — or about his wife, Agnes Turnbull who is not mentioned. The stone is entirely impersonal.

Thrughstanes

No coped stone in Stirling now bears any legible inscription (10). The few which survive almost all have skull, bones, hourglasses (the so-called Emblems of Mortality) and robed Angels blowing trumpets, the Angels of the Resurrection. All give the impression of antiquity and some may well be 16th century. Early 17th century slabs are narrow, sometimes tapered, and if there is an inscription it is often written round the margins of the stone. Later ones are wider and cut square, with the inscription running across the width.

The earliest slab in Stirling is dated 1579 (Plate 2, Mitchell No. 182). It has a raised, central panel and the incised date may be a later addition or have been recut. Raised above the surface is a shield charged for Gibb, 'In chief a broken spear, chevronwise, held by a hand issuing from the sinister; in base a spur' (RCAHMS). There is a hammer or mallet, ? a chisel and a pick and the initials MG JG and ET. This is one of four stones, all for members of the Gibb family, enclosed by a low, stone parapet or crib, also incised with the name Gibb and dated 1880. The late 16th century records mention a number of Gibbs who were quarriers, including a James, employed 'winning stones' in 1575/6 (11) and a John, who married his servant, Jonet Brand in 1592 (12).

Close by is a much wider slab (Plate 3, Mitchell No. 153) enclosed by another crib. It is un-dated, has a shield containing an elaborate reversed 4, indicating that the original owner was a merchant, and the initials RG and MT. Below are later inscriptions for Elizabeth Gibb, her husband a Chisholm and other 19th century Chisholms. Almost certainly this stone was originally placed for Robert Gibb, a prominent Stirling merchant of the later 17th century, and his wife Margaret Thomson. Gibb was closely associated with the resurgent Presbyterians of Stirling in 1689, petitioning the Privy Council on their behalf. The Gibbs lived in the former house of the Earl of Linlithgow, on what is now St. John Street. Robert died in late 1689 or early 1690. His widow was 'host' to the political prisoner Stirling of Auchyle in 1690 (13). The inscriptions on the other stones within these cribs are eloquent of the continuing local prestige of this family for 400 years.

Nearby is another slab with a shield but with a fuller inscription (Mitchell No. 172); HERE LIES THE CORPSE OF ANDREW BAIRD BAILLIE IN STIRLING WHO DIED 24 JUNE 1692 AGED 77. MARGARAT SWORD HIS SPOUSE DIED 28 MARCH 1677. Baird's right to the thrughstane recently erected in the kirkyard was ratified on 5th September 1676.

Headstones

It has previously been thought that the earliest surviving dated headstones in Stirling were two identical and damaged specimens, dated 1674 (Plate 4, Mitchell Nos. 198 and 199). However, I think it probable that the Service stone (Mitchell No. 136) previously dated to 1697 by the RCAHMS, is the earliest. It is certainly by far the largest and most impressive (Plate 5 and Figures 2 and 3). It is mounted on a masonry base and consists of two parts, the upper of which has been removed and replaced the wrong way round. On the western side, encircled by a serpent, symbol of eternity, are three figures; 'speech balloons' issue from the mouths of the outer two, though the words are largely illegible; an upright feature, perhaps a tree, divides the circle and the 'angel' on the right may not be directly connected with the scene on the left. The scene was identified by Willsher and Hunter (14) and was published by Francis Quarles in 1635 (15).

Only the foreground of Quarles' engraving appears on the stone. The figure on the left covers its face in horror whilst pointing to a sun dial. The other, winged and enhaloed, has its left arm at the first's waist, brooking no delay. On the ground is an hour-glass. Quarles accompanies the engraving by a quotation from Job and a long verse, a lament for untimely, approaching death; but he ends with the true moral —

> Fear'st thou to go, when such an Arme invites thee?
> Dread'st thou thy load of sin? or what affrights thee?
> If thou begin to feare, they fear begins;
> Foole, can he beare thee hence, and not thy sins?

The angel blowing a trumpet, which now appears at the top of the eastern face would originally have crowned this scene.

The eastern face is now eroded and largely unintelligible; top left is a skull, top right a hand holding what may be the 'Thread of Life'; down the sides are a mason's tools. The long inscription is largely illegible but it refers to a John Service, who died in 16(??) and who was married to a woman called Bessie, whose surname is also illegible, though readings have included Buine and Ewine. Both sides are marked by pits, several centimetres across, said to be the result of musket shot. Who was John Service, when did he die and why should a gravestone be shot at — on both sides? Of the three John Services in Stirling during the 17th century only the first can have been buried beside a wife called Bessie. He was a mason, admitted burgess in 1604 and dead by 1636 . . . when his son also John, also a mason, was given a licence by the Kirk Session, to set up a stone over his grave, a decision ratified a year later. I would read his age as 54 rather than the 74 suggested by RCAHMS. A contract of marriage for the younger John (16) shows that his mother was Bessie Ewing, one of the readings previously suggested for the spouse of the older John.

If the true date of the stone is 1637, then it is easy to believe that the pits were made during Monk's siege of the Castle from the Holy Rude kirk tower in 1651; both those buildings bear very similar pits, generally accepted as the result of musket fire. The stone, on a direct line between the two, would have provided excellent cover during sniping forays. The new, early date also suggests that perhaps John Service, the fashionable young mason who was soon to be employed drawing the draft for the portrait statue of John Cowane which stands over Cowane's Hospital doorway, made this stone as a demonstration of his skill, of how practical the new headstones were. If so, his lead was not followed; certainly no imitations survive. John Service died in 1645, a plague year – but there are no surviving headstones from 1637 to 1676, the date of an identical pair of stones, reminiscent of the many such pairs found at Logie (Plate 4). On their eastern faces are the skull and bones and the mis-spelt motto; on the West, identical lists of unidentified initials. These are less sophisticated than the generality of surviving Stirling headstones.

The next surviving headstone, however (Plate 6, Mitchell No. 145) (or a missing predecessor) did set a fashion. It is dated 1696 in raised relief and though it is incised 'John Foreman Margaret Lakie 1779', this is obvious, later addition. Also in raised relief are a skull and crossed bones, standard Emblems of Mortality, and an hour-glass, with some eroded greenery above; on the other side is a reversed 4 and a wreath-like ring of greenery, with a malt shovel and three rather stylised sheaves of corn. Evidently the original owner was one of the numerous merchant malt-men. Several of these symbols appear on later stones in the series, but it is the 'shoulders' of these stones which are so characteristic. In each case they form a distinctive double S scroll, unique to the 15 similar stones in Stirling. Those dated prior to 1707 are noted by RCAHMS as 'large, ornate headstones', though otherwise their similarity is not remarked on. They carry primary dates from 1696 to 1737. The details of design, the standard of workmanship and the quality of the stone all vary but probably all were made by one mason or by a master and his successor.

On all the early members of the series the central motif, between the 'shoulders' is an ornamental rosette; but on our next example (Plate 7, Mitchell No. 179) this has become a winged face, the Winged Soul, leaving the body at the moment of death. On the western side is an even more bizarre face (Plate 8), horned and with ribbon-like streamers flowing from its mouth and forming 'knots' which support a central tablet with the dividers and set square of a wright. Also on this face is an incised inscription; HERE LYES THE CORPS OF ROBERT FERGUSSON LATE BAILLIE IN STIRLING WHO DIED 3 MARCH 1695 AGED 41. Robert Fergusson was admitted burgess and guildbrother of Stirling on 22nd February 1692, the son of John Fergusson, the town's first tobacco pipe maker (17). Robert's brother David (whose initials appear in raised relief on the eastern side) was admitted burgess in 1694. On 20th April 1678 Robert had appeared before the Burgh Court accused of leading a riot or insurrection of the town's prentices. The causes of this riot are obscure but probably it had political overtones, forcing Robert to lie low till he emerged as a magistrate under the new presbyterian regime of the 1690s.

On one stone in the series dated 1724 (Plate 9, Mitchell No. 135) the S scrolls have been modified to form birds' heads — probably pelicans which mythically and heraldically feed their young on blood from their own breast and so are emblematic of the self-sacrifice of Christ. On another (Mitchell No. 160 not illustrated) the central rosette has become a well cut flower, perhaps a poppy, another popular image of sleep and death. The finest of the double S Series (Plate 10 unnumbered in Mitchell but adjacent to Nos. 158 and 169) is dated 1728 and probably belonged to James Stevenson, merchant of Stirling, who was given permission to set up a stone in May of that year. Like other fashionable inhabitants of the town, James (IS) and his wife (IC, full name unknown) could visit their own gravestone, already inscribed. People who set up their gravestones before their death would not have them inscribed 'Here lies . . .' or 'In memory of . . .'; and in that age of precise religious orthodoxy 'Sacred to the memory of . . .' would have been condemned as idolatry. Nor were claims of personal virtue admissible; modesty apart, virtue was irrelevant to salvation, which flowed from God's Grace alone; virtue could not save. The lack of words is symptomatic of a terse and conventional age.

If Stevenson and his family did come to look at their stone then what they saw was a parable, a summary of the orthodox meaning of life and death. Death, the one certain fact of life, still lies in the future, only its time and consequences open to doubt. MEMENTO MORI (Remember you will die) the stone tells them. Above the words a winged hour-glass wordlessly reminds them that Time Flies; Time is a feature of current, human life, not of the eternity which will follow death and it is in this Time that IS and IC live, their relationship not expressed in words but by the conventional juxtaposition of their initials. Perhaps they will overcome death; for above the hour-glass is a spray of leaves, palm fronds, symbolic of victory over death. And on all these stones are swags of greenery, indicative of Heaven. Stevenson's stone is topped by a rosette but on others, such as the Fergusson stone already mentioned, the top is occupied by a Winged Soul.

Whilst MEMENTO MORI indicates a future certainty, the Winged Soul is only one possible sequel of death, for it was only the souls of the Elect, those chosen by God, even before birth for an eternity of bliss, which would make the heaven-ward journey. Another hopeful symbol seen on many graves, though not in this series, are Angels of the Resurrection, blowing their trumpets. But hope was only for the Elect. Death, with its concomitant decay, is symbolised below by the skull and bones and on some graves (though again not on the Double S series), by the sexton's tools or the figure of Death himself. But death and decay are of little consequence for the Elect; at the last day even their bodies would rise again, whole and perfectly restored. But for the damned — the vast majority of human kind — death and decay were but a prefiguring of the eternal torments of Hell. Death is not the end. It is a nodal point, a crux at which Time is divided from Eternity, the saved from the damned.

This is the point made almost explicit by the inscription on the Simson stone (Mitchell No. 177), a stone which re-illustrates several points already made. It has some features in common with the Double S stones and falls well within the period but the S scrolls are lacking. On the eastern face, in raised relief, are the initials IS and IL together with a pruning hook encircled by a serpent; below this the ribbon once said MEMENTO MORI, and if the stone were raised, we would find skull and bones below. On the western face (Plate 11) are a gardener's spade, shears and what is probably a rake; a faint incised inscription tells us that it is the grave of John Simson, who died aged 55 on the 27th March 1724. There is also the following couplet:

AS SEEDS WHEN SOWN DO DIE BEFORE THEY LIVE
I DIED IN HOPES THIS BODY WOULD REVIVE

John Simson, gardener in Cambuskenneth, had applied for a licence for a stone before his death, though permission had been delayed till 20th April 1726; this is the date of the primary raised inscription on the eastern face. (In a few cases, particularly where a licence was granted late in the year, the date may be that of the following year; so presumably the date is strictly that when the stone was set up.) Although the tools and the couplet are obviously related to Simson's prestigious calling of gardener, they are not in any way personal to him; the sentiments are entirely conventional. Simson's simple stone, in fact, tells us as much and as little about its owner as did McCulloch's grand one.

THE SIGNIFICANCE OF THE STONES

We have seen some important ways in which these stones differ from modern ones. Firstly, they convey their message rather through symbols than words; secondly, even the most elaborate are surprisingly impersonal; and thirdly, the stones anticipate death, rather than recording it. One reason for purchasing and setting up a stone prior to death was simple practicality; people made the arrangements at a time when they were feeling fairly well off. A gravestone was bound to come in handy one day . . . MEMENTO MORI; neither the poverty of old age nor the parsimony of the survivors could thwart the owner's wish for a stone. Another was that the stone affirmed ownership of the plot, so often the subject of bitter dispute. Particularly in the Hillfoots area, inscriptions often state that the the stone marks the intended burial place of a named couple and their children! What is still unclear is why this type of stone, marking ownership, is confined to a narrow belt across central Scotland. (6) But I think we can now begin to explain the wider issue of the increasing popularity of gravestones in the 17th and 18th centuries. Of course, it was partly a reflection of increased wealth and of new designs bringing cheaper stones within the means of a wider public. But that would only partly explain why the extra cash was expended in this particulary way.

Ownership, it will be recalled, was not merely personal; it was familial. And the heads of families who were setting up stones in the 17th and early 18th centuries were the sort of people who were purchasing private pews in the kirk at the same time. The position of these private pews closely mirrored the social standing of their owners; prestigious families had the pews closest to the pulpit, or even a private loft. And there is an obvious comparison between the bitterness of disputes about gravestones and those about pew ownership. The connection is graphically underlined by a dispute in Logie in 1593, when two men crept into the church at night and destroyed the pew recently set up by David Balfour of Powhouse, 'because the same stood on their forbears bones', that is, over the family burial plot in the kirk (18). These, then, were men (I have encountered only one application from a woman) who no longer wished to mix with their fellows in the body of the kirk for the sermon, but to sit apart with their families and peers, men who no longer traded as a group but as increasingly competitive individuals and men who did not want to be huddled into an anonymous pit when they died but to remain distinct and individual, part of their family but not of the crowd.

Those who had previously had marked burial plots in the kirk were the landed elite; their stones bore heraldic devices, which sometimes also appear on slabs and coped stones in the kirkyard. In setting up gravestones, the rising middle ranks of society were consciously aping their social superiors, claiming that they too had property, family, and the right to assert a carefully orthodox view of the meaning of life and death. Death, ubiquitous death, was the nodal point between Time and Eternity and would divide the Elect from the damned. It was the focus of elaborate ceremony; 17th century Scottish funerals were often ruinously expensive displays of conspicuous consumption. (19) It was a natural concentration of attention on the time which, according to contemporary ideology, so critically divides society into the saved and the damned, the ultimate winners and the losers in the race of life. As the owner contemplated his gravestone, a status symbol formerly confined to the elite, he surely did so with a certain self-satisfaction, perhaps in the hope that he would one day be seen as the founder of a dynasty, and in the hope or even the belief that worldly success would be followed by that heavenward flight to eternal bliss. All around each distinguished stone were un-marked graves; to the North side of every church was an area devoid of stones, reserved for the poor, the outcast and the stranger. And the message which is not inscribed or incised but is implicit in the fact of each stone, is that the owner has the wealth and the power to distinguish himself and his family from that anonymous mass and to assert his new view of individuality, even from the grave.

ACKNOWLEDGEMENTS

It is a pleasure to acknowledge, once again, my debt to George Dixon of Central Region Archives and to other staff there and at the Scottish Record Office, Glasgow University, and Stirling District Libraries. I am particularly indebted to Betty Willsher for invaluable comments on an early draft of this paper, which have saved me from several blunders; her knowledge of Scottish gravestones is, of course, unrivalled. The editor, Lindsay Corbett, has been as helpful as ever, in particular in that detailed checking of the manuscript which saves the reader from confusions and uncertainties. Errors remain inalienably my own!

REFERENCES AND NOTES

1. The main published sources used in the Introduction are:
   - a ARIES, P. Western Attitudes to Death; from the Middle Ages to the Present. Marion Boyars, London. 1976.
   - b BURGESS, F. English Churchyard Memorials. Lutterworth Press. 1963.
   - c CHRISTISON, D. The carvings and inscriptions on the kirkyard monuments of the Scottish Lowlands; particularly in Perth, Fife, Angus, Mearns and Lothian. *Proceedings of the Society of Antiquaries of Scotland* Vol XXXVI, 1901-02, pp 280-457.
   - d WILLSHER, B. Understanding Scottish Graveyards. Chambers, Edinburgh. 1985.
   - e Royal Commission on the Ancient and Historical Monuments of Scotland; Stirlingshire. HMSO. 1963. Cited as RCAHMS.
2. The inscriptions of most of the stones in the kirk and the kirkyard are recorded in MITCHELL, J. F. and S. Monumental Inscriptions (pre-1855). East Stirlingshire – Scottish Genealogy Society, 1972. I indicate the number assigned by the Mitchells on first mentioning each stone. Cited as Mitchell.
3. Central Region Archives (CRA). Stirling Kirk Session Minutes CH2/1026/Series, quoted by date. Where information about date of death has been used it has usually been based on the Registers of Testaments, Scottish Record Office (SRO), Commissariot of Stirling, CC21/5 Series.
4. CRA. Logie Kirk Session Minutes CH2/1001/1 and CH2/1001/7.
5. RCAHMS.
6. I am particularly indebted to Betty Willsher for the information that this practice of setting up stones during the owner's life is confined to the former counties of Stirling, Clackmannan, Renfrew and Dunbarton; elsewhere in Scotland stones were commemmorative.
7. *Stirling Observer* 6th August 1857 page 3. Letter from Charles Rogers. His assurance that mural monuments would be preserved when the old kirkyard dyke was demolished was ignored.
8. Engraving of East and West Churches, Stirling, in Light Views of Stirling with Notices by Robert Chambers. 1830.
9. *Stirling Observer* 4th October 1989 page 11.
10. I here ignore Mitchell No. 131 which is a 19th century reconstruction.
11. CRA/SRO, Stirling Common Good Accounts 1575 6, E82/55/9.

12. Stirling Parochial Registers; Marriages. *Northern Notes and Queries or The Scottish Antiquary* Vol VI, p 167.
13. Register of the Privy Council of Scotland, 1689 Third Series, Vol XIV, Edinburgh, 1933. Passim.
14. WILLSHER, Betty and HUNTER, Doreen. Stones: a Guide to some remarkable eighteenth century gravestones. Canongate, Edinburgh, 1978.
15. QUARLES, Francis. Emblems Divine and Moral. London, 1635.
16. CRA. Burgh Register of Deeds, B66/9/3 Contract of Marriage registered 1st September 1634 and dated 21st July 1634.
17. CRA. Council Record, B66/20/5. 1st October 1664 and 9th January 1671.
18. MENZIES FERGUSSON, R. A Parish History of Logie. Paisley, 1905 Vol 2, page 93.
19. GORDON, Anne. Death is for the Living. Paul Harris Publishing, 1984.

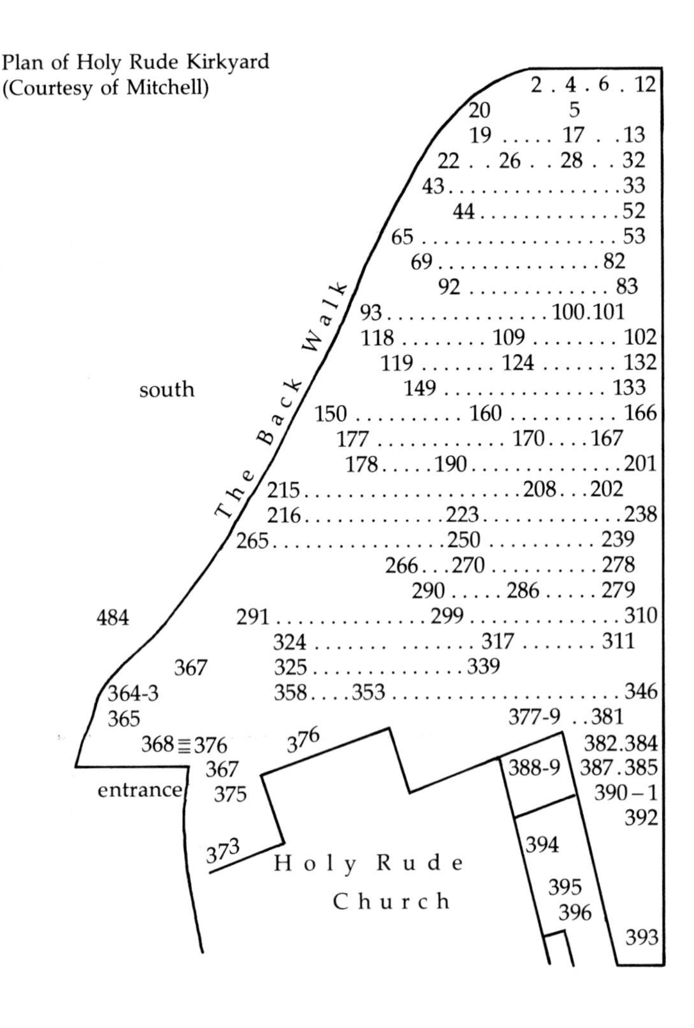

Plan of Holy Rude Kirkyard
(Courtesy of Mitchell)

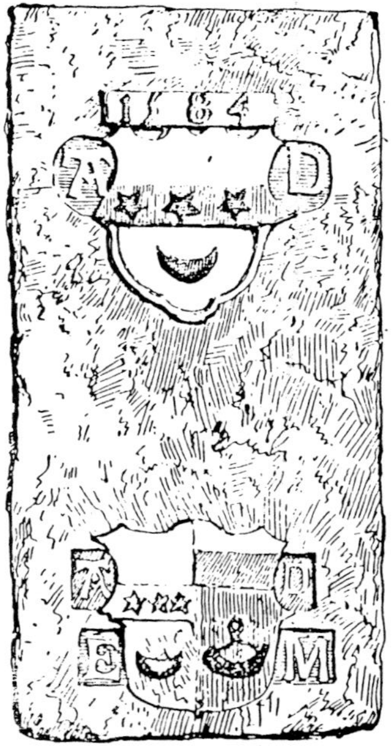

Figure 1. Drawing of the tomb of Alexander Durham of Mollet and wife Elizabeth Murray (Mitchell No. 462), Holy Rude, dated 1584 — has initials and Coats of Arms. (from Fleming, J. S. The Old Castle Vennel and its Inhabitants, Stirling.

Figure 2. Service Stone; drawing of central motif, on western face, from Christison. The serpent, twined on itself, a symbol of eternal life, appears on two other stones of gardeners (including the Simson) – may have some other significance.

Figure 3. Illustration from Quarles, 1635 — the inspiration for the left half of the Servicestone central motif; there are few other examples recorded in Scotland of the use of patterns from Emblem Books. (Courtesy of Glasgow University Library)

Plate 1. A coped stone, near the kirk tower.

Plate 2. Stirling's oldest dated stone, a narrow slab 1579, unusually combines heraldic and occupational symbols. The heraldry shows it belonged to the Gibb family (see p 83).

Plate 3. Typical late 17th century slab is wider. The initials, added names and later adjacent stones imply it was set up for Robert Gibb and his wife Margaret Thomson (see p 83).

Plate 4. One of two identical stones, dated 1674. Paired stones are particularly common at Logie.

Plate 5. The Service Stone, eastern face. The extensive inscription was both above and below the central motif.

Plate 6. Earliest of the Double S series, original owner unknown.

Plate 7. The Fergusson stone, eastern face.

Plate 8. The Fergusson stone, western face, with inscription and bizarre face.

Plate 9. Unusual – for 'Pelicans' whose mythical self sacrifice mirrors that of Christ, and for having only one set of initials instead of a pair.

Plate 10. An exceptionally fine stone — the Stevensons were a prestigious family.

Plate 11. Eastern face of Simson stone — a pruning hook! encircled by a serpent plus Emblems of Mortality. The inscription can now only be read in direct evening sunshine.

PEOPLE OF THE FORTH (4)

WHO WAS CHARLES ROGERS?

J. Malcolm Allan
University of Strathclyde

Who was Charles Roger = R O G E R ? He was born in 1825 and seems to exist until c.1855. That is not the only question. Who was Charles Rogers = R O G E R S ? He seems to have existed from c.1855 and he certainly died in 1890. So, who was Charles Rodger = R O D G E R ? He seems to exist in the Stirling District Council's mind as a street name in Bridge of Allan: Charles Rodger Place. And, finally, who was Charles Rodgers = R O D G E R S ? He appears only in a mis-spelled index entry to the *Stirling Journal.*

To unravel these four men I shall concentrate on the first two; they existed as the same man consecutively. The second two are also the same man as the first two give or take inventive spelling. So, the four men are really just one.

I acknowledge help from the following sources and people. The late Provost Steel many years ago donated his own copy of *Leaves from my autobiography* by Charles Rogers (1876) to the Dr W. H. Welsh Educational and Historical Trust. From my own shelves I have used a copy of *The serpent's track* by Charles Rogers (1880), a rare pamphlet I bought from Ginny Wills, Bridge of Allan Books about 100 years after publication. The Keeper of Muniments at St. Andrews University helpfully transcribed an obituary from one Fife newspaper and provided an execrable print from a microfilm from another. In the Manuscripts Department of the National Library of Scotland I had access to 570 sheets of letters to Rogers and with great difficulty read all the scratchy, scrawling writing. From Stirling District Libraries and other libraries, including my own at the University of Strathclyde I have used books written by Rogers or published by him.

The year 1990 is the centenary of the death of this single and singular man: Charles Rogers, D.D. (College of William & Mary, Maryland), reputed D.D. (St. Andrews in 1881 — but they know nothing of it), LL.D. (Columbia College, New York). I suggested it would make a topic for a paper expecting another to do it. That was not fruitful, and I end up doing it myself. I never learn.

He was a man of words, spoken and written, in fact of millions of words so I shall use no illustrations or slides. Such a man merits yet more words.

Charles Rogers was born, as Charles R.O.G.E.R., at Dunino in Fife in 1825. His father was 57 and his mother 21. She died in the childbirth.

They had been married just two years. Rev. James Roger, R.O.G.E.R. please note, had been minister of Dunino since 1805 and he continued there until 1849. Before that, since he was born in 1767, he had been schoolmaster, as were many proto-ministers, journalist, first editor of the *Dundee Advertiser*, private secretary to an M.P., and a writer in London. He wrote at least two books and many leader articles in papers and left a manuscript historical novel at his death. His brother, Charles also wrote at least 2 books, mainly genealogical and religious, and was Librarian of Dundee public library. This was a literary family off old farming stock. Of his father, Charles Rogers says ''as a preacher he did not excel'' . . . and for 44 years in Dunino kirk at that!

Charles, the motherless bairn, was brought up at Dunino Manse by his father's sister, who must have been a middle aged or elderly woman; he was educated by his father and also at the parish school. He was not allowed out of their sight unaccompanied and forbidden to stray beyond the parish boundary, just 2 square miles. He says he grew up rude in speech and rough in manners. It sounds solitary, introverted and dull.

By the age of 11 he had escaped into the realm of books, not just the boyish reading of Holinshed's *Scottish Chronicle,* the 16th century source for Shakespeare when writing Macbeth. The church officer gave him Harry the Minstrel's *Wallace* to read, early Scottish verse followed up by Barbour's *The Bruce*. That is tough and heady stuff for a confined boy. He soon set about collecting ballads from the domestics and history books even mastering the handwriting of the Dunino Kirk registers which went back to 1643. His father read Greek and Latin text daily all his life and taught him the Classics. It was his father who then determined that Charles should be a minister as there was no money to apprentice him or prepare him for a profession.

At 14, with a bursary, he went to St. Andrew's University. It was 1839 and he later confessed to being ''a poor student'' for 7 years. He was there to study Arts and Divinity but spent most of his time reading Scottish literature and history in the University library and he never cites a St Andrew's degree after his name.

By 1840, only 15 and one year at University, he was writing for 4 local newspapers on Scottish topics, including in the *Dundee Courier*, and he published his first pamphlet, supporting capital punishments. He wrote for the next 50 years. By 1843, at the year of the Disruption of the Church of Scotland, as an abominable brat of 18 he challenged the right of the Principal to remain in office because he was a seceding elder. He did it by pseudonymous letters to the papers, for and against, writing as if lawyer or clergyman, all by himself. The topic caused a stir that took it to the Senatus and the Presbytery before the furore died down. It is indicative of the combative and quirky nature in later life and the command of learning all his life.

The year before, in 1842 and aged 17, he had bought at auction, a 17th century manuscript which turned out to be the lost poems of a Scottish poet, Sir Robert Aytoun. By 1844, still a student and only 19, he had corresponded with literary scholars and then edited the poems to publish his first book. He presented his father with a copy without telling him about it as he knew he disapproved of all except classical and religious studies. From then on he visited local historic sites around Fife and wrote articles on them and on St. Andrews. At home, solitary and without companions, he said he studied 12 hours a day, as did his father.

On completion of his University courses he was licensed to preach in 1846. One of his first temporary posts was as assistant to Dr Hew Scott, that most learned editor of the *Fasti,* for which he was paid 9 shillings a week. Then followed a series of short-stay clergy posts in Fife, including assisting his ailing father then over 80.

The year 1849 brought certain success – he was appointed minister of the North Church, Dunfermline; his father died, in debt, aged 83; and he published a *History of St. Andrews* based on his articles and researches which was well received, reviewed and the 1,000 copies sold rapidly. Perhaps as a result, in 1850 he was elected a Fellow of the Society of Antiquaries of Scotland and with the profits he visited the areas of his boyhood heroes, The Bruce and Wallace, touring the sites around Stirling, Bannockburn and Falkirk.

He was 25 and was invited to write a book about Airthrey Spa. This is the Bridge of Allan connection and the book he wrote in 1851 was *A week at Bridge of Allan.* It was a promotion job commissioned by Major Henderson of Westerton. He got £20 for doing it, the equivalent of a quarter year's salary as a minister. Major Henderson, for such was the style of the man, stipulated what went in and how to write it! It is not entirely accurate as a result. Some of it is the Major's unfulfilled plans and fancies, including the map of places that were never built. The first edition, published by Lizars, was 1,000 copies as was the St. Andrew's book. In all it went to 10 editions of larger or lesser size in 13 years and some were sold direct by Rogers who signs the receipts of sale to individuals, signing as "Charles Roger". We know it was done in 1851 since there exists a letter to Rogers from Major Henderson dated 1 April 1851 (NLS 14303/72):

Mr Dear Revd. Sir,

I have your kind letter of the 27th and I am glad you propose coming to visit me at Westerton and I will tell all abt. the plans. and friendly remarks and wishes of Lord and Lady Abercromby when we meet. The principal remark being that your style is far too full of laudatory remarks which you may remember what I myself wished to impress upon you too. However you can easily draw that *milder* I daresay. Another wish was to have out all, or at all event a good bit, abt. Sir

Archibald Christie, burying ground at old Logie Kirk, so that is easily managed too (I'll tell you why when we meet). Mr John Fletcher will have got the 1st proof sheets by this time and will be doing your bidding.
I return to Westerton on Saturday forenoon (I leave London on Friday 9 a.m.) will be happy to see you there at dinner and stay there till further orders so please make your arrangements accordingly, and come as soon as you can.

Henderson is calling the shots. Fletcher may be of *Fletcher's St. Andrew's Guide* and be involved with Lizars and the engraved title page of 1851 or illustrations. The letter-press title page has the date 1852 behind it in most editions.

At the time Rogers was assistant minister at Ballingry, Fife, and after another year as mission minister at Carnoustie, he came to live in Bridge of Allan in January 1853. He stayed 2 years and in the April began a monthly newspaper *The Bridge of Allan Journal and Spa Directory.* It ran for only a few issues. In May 1854 he opened a preaching station in Bridge of Allan. The parish churches were a distance away at Logie and Lecropt. The only church in the village was the Free Church of 1843 and the Episcopal Church was just starting a summer mission and congregation. Rogers was always an established church man, plain Church of Scotland with protestant and Covenanter overtones. It was in 1854, in December, that he married a St. Andrews girl but there were no children to the marriage which lasted until 1880.

The preaching station, like many of his ventures, did not last long. In January 1855 he accepted the post as Chaplain to the Stirling Castle garrison. At this time, of the Crimean War, it was a busy camp and Stirling partly a military town. When he left Bridge of Allan to take up residence in the Chaplain's quarters, a wing of The Argyle Lodging, he was given a public breakfast by the inhabitants, a silver claret jug and a purse of sovereigns. He records, on taking up his new post, that in the previous 9 years he earned by preaching £266/16/6, an average of £30 per year, but his books and writings must have been a further source of income.

That is the Bridge of Allan connection . . . . or is it? In his book *A week at Bridge of Allan* he wrote in 1851 (p. 39/40):

It has been often lamented by patriotic and right-minded Scotsmen, that no monument worthy of the subject has been erected to commemmorate the gallant deeds and heroic achievements of Wallace, the most popular and meritorious of Scottish heroes. Than the highest point of Abbey Craig, certainly a more suitable site for such an erection, could not be suggested . . . . . Mr Patric Park, the distinguished sculptor, has recently executed a magnificent model of a colossal statue of the hero . . . . Such a monument, it is scarcely necessary to remark, would be peculiarly suitable for the summit of Abbey Craig; and we hope the period is not distant, when by the liberal subscriptions of patriotic Scotsmen, this or some other approved monument to the memory of Wallace, will decorate its crest . . . It is proper to state, that Mr Macfarlane of Coneyhill, to whose munificent liberality at Bridge of Allan we have already had occasion to allude, has generously offered to head a subscription list with fifty pounds, for the erection of a monument to Wallace at the top of Abbey Craig . . . .

The Wallace of his boyhood still dominated his thoughts, almost becoming an obseesion. The result is there for all to see – The Wallace Monument. It is now quite different from the description of Park's statue but it is within the parish of Logie and even appears on some early postcards as 'Wallace Monument, Bridge of Allan' which is where Rogers had the idea of a site in 1851.

From 1855 – 1863 he was in Stirling. Although garrison chaplain the position at Stirling Castle seems to have overtaken him as a historic site and means of glory rather than just a parish. As Scottish history obsessed him he became beset by controversy and conflict of interest. It was never to leave him until his death in 1890.

By now he was Rogers, R.O.G.E.R.S., assuming the name without explanation. The "S" he assumed might almost stand for 'Scotland' for which he became a promoter of projects, a man of monuments and a writer. As a clergyman, like his father, he is not memorable.

By 1855 Stirling Town Council was a very corrupt body. It had effected 'economy' by not paying for a police force and reverted to a night watch where local householders each took turn, or got a drunken idler to do it for them at 2 shillings a night. The result was prostitution, gaming and general mayhem all round the Castle area, the Top of the Town and near the Church of the Holy Rude, the Valley and the Ladies Rock; in fact on Rogers' doorstep.

When Rogers was told it was his turn for the Watch he took exception and decided to clean up the area. Among the things he proposed was a Cemetery Company to extend the old Holy Rude cemetery into The Valley. He managed to do this by 1857 completing it as it is now with various monuments, all encouraged by Rogers in a 2 year campaign against objections. John Macfarlane of Coneyhill underwrote the lease on the land; others suscribed to monuments – The Pyramid, John Knox, Guthrie, the Wigton Martyrs in a glass cage. These were his Reformation and Presbyterian heroes for which he cajoled the gentry and prominent businessmen into paying by raising suscriptions, a method he used from then on. The Holy Rude area was cleared and the Bowling Green wall lowered to improve the place.

A taste for monuments set in and with it his first Wallace monument, a statue on the Atheneum building where it looks down King Street, in 1858. His next proposal was for laying out the King's Park and restoring the King's Knot Garden. By 1859 he had set up The Stirling Improvement Society, one of many societies he was to father. His 1861 proposal for a public Hall failed otherwise there might have been a Rogers or Wallace Hall instead of the present Albert Hall of later years. With this high profile of public works, in contrast to the then councillors, Rogers was himself elected to the Town Council. His proposed tree planting; baths; lavatories; libraries and dwellings for the working classes never came about until 30 years later.

By now he was Dr Rogers, using the LL.D. obtained somehow from Columbia College, New York and which was questioned many times during his lifetime. His main proposal from 1851 was for a Wallace Monument on Abbey Craig. The general idea of a monument began elsewhere, in 1818 and before Rogers was born, but the 1851 proposal of the site was his and already supported by John Macfarlane of Coneyhill. By 1856 he had set up a committee, one of his many committees, to promote the project and raise subscriptions for it. Members included some important men from far and wide, among them one, William Burns, a Glasgow writer or solicitor of some power. He was a Scottish patriot but very anti-English and, as it soon transpired, anti-Rogers. At every committee meeting, over six years, there was controversy with Burns. It started over the minutes, the accounts, the design, the competition, the method of funding and particularly over subscriptions. Rogers, as Secretary, with unbounded energy for Wallace, set up agents and committees in all parts of Scotland and beyond in Birmingham, Manchester, Liverpool and London. Rogers stumped the country in his vacations, a means made easier by the network of trains now fanned out from Stirling. It is a story in itself and not a happy one.

At last in 1861 the foundation stone was laid. Such was the enthusiasm that Rogers had stirred up that 100,000 people turned up and the procession was two miles long. Another part of his energy has been recorded. Of the £13,000 needed to complete the monument by 1869 Rogers raised over £7,000 or more than half of it personally. His own salary as Chaplain was £74 per annum with a free house, raised later to £150. Also on record is the method he employed. It is stated that he personally wrote 20,000 letters in a five-year period which was computed at 3,333 hours work or 83½ days per year. In addition he composed and sent thousands of printed circulars.

I said he was a man of many words; those letters represent one part of one project begun and take no account of the committees and refutations of Burns' allegations. The Burns vendetta continued until Burns died in 1876, always casting up aspects of the Wallace Monument activity in whatever and wherever Rogers undertook.

His Stirling improvements and the Wallace campaigns stirred up another vendetta from Provost Dick and an editor of the *Stirling Observer*. In 1861 the Provost petitioned the War Office to remove Rogers from the post of Chaplain to the garrison. The Chaplain General held a Court of Inquiry at Stirling Castle which disproved all the charges. Rogers sued the Provost for libel, the first of several libel cases he brought and won, and the Provost was voted off the Town Council at the same time as Rogers was voted on.

The high drama dogged the foundation stone laying also when a Burns protegé, gained access to the celebration banquet on a false ticket and caused a disturbance which ended in police intervention! Rogers had had enough of Burns' machinations and a few days later resigned as Secretary of the Committee. In an unwise move he set up a Supplementary Committee of his own since he did not give up fundraising. It led to further allegations and was repeated, lesson unlearned, with other projects.

To improve his own finances and engage his literary talents as well, Rogers set up a printing office in Stirling. It eventually employed 14 people and he began a newspaper *The Stirling Gazette* in 1862. It ran for 14 months but overextended his capacity as a businessman. When one of his employees, a boy, was bribed by a rival to say that it was bankrupt it coincided with the libel case. Although he won against Provost Dick the costs far outweighed the damages awarded. The paper folded and to prevent being made bankrupt by his 96 creditors he resigned as Chaplain in 1863 and fled to sanctuary at Holyrood Abbey until a deal was worked out. He lived in Edinburgh a while, again hounded by Burns' innuendo, and in 1864 left for a literary career in London, with debts and a persecution complex. He was aged 38.

He was already a religious writer and publisher using his own printing shop when in Stirling. While still in Bridge of Allan in 1853 he had begun *Tracts for Sunday Schools*, a series that evolved into his next scenario. From 1860 *Stirling Castle Tracts*, aimed specificially at the military, were produced and disseminated. By 1862/3 three journals were added: *The Workman's Friend: The Briton;*and *The Recorder.* Erratically produced and simultaneous with his Wallace activities, these eventually failed, some after only a few issues.

After he left Stirling for London he visited towns in Scotland, England and Ireland setting up 150 distribution points for tracts and even had 30 outlets in the colonies. By now the enterprise evolved into the *Naval and Military Tract Society*, with 1000 supporters and subscribers. Rogers, of course, was Secretary, writer and publisher at £1 per week and travelling expenses. It became the *London Book and Tract Depository* and lasted until 1874. Some records survive showing print runs. Over a short period 950,000 tracts and 89,000 journals had been published and distributed.

The Burns vendetta cropped up here, as each new publication came out. Also through Dr Baxter of the rival Religious Tract Society Rogers was anonymously denounced in 1866 and his accounts investigated. Rival tract agents pursued him and allegations were printed and repeated in national papers: that he had absconded with the Wallace Monument funds and even that he had committed suicide in remorse for absconding! None of it was true but all of it stuck and muddied the waters as his subscription seeking for one enterprise overlapped the timescale of the other and sometimes the same agents were involved.

Incredibly, he also engaged in literary and historical research, editing and publishing many works. While still in Stirling between 1855 and 1857 he had compiled *The Modern Scottish Minstrel* in six volumes and written 200 memoirs of the authors used. It had a moral side as well as he intended that it should be of decent verse, not questionable ballads, and be seen as continuing the strain of the 18th century poets. His profit was £50 but he got a further £20 when passing on the copyright to another publisher. After a hiatus of literary output overtaken by his Wallace and religious tract work in 1867 came out *Lyra Britannica* with 232 memoirs of hymn writers, closely followed by other hymn and poetry collections.

Again, back in Stirling in 1855 he had founded the *Scottish Literary Institute* to promote Scottish letters. It fell foul of William Burns and was refounded in 1861 as the *Caledonia Institute* which included aiming for pensions and recompense for writers. The fact that this was happening at the same time as this Stirling improvements and Wallace work is wonder enough without another enterprise for Scotland, the *Churchyard Improvement Association*. Both these folded as he left Scotland but the ideas recur.

Longest and most successful was *The Grampian Club* founded in 1868, with himself as Secretary and Editor. The purpose was to research and publish Scottish literature and history from a London base. The beginning of this is his first book in 1844 when 19 and still a student. In 1868 there was another periodical *The Oak* which ran six months as the pace and enthusiasm mounted. The Historical Society, later the Royal Historical Society, was started in 1868, some say by Rogers other with Rogers in the van. By 1870 he was the Secretary with a salary and had been acting secretary since the start. He was also the editor and 'Historiographer'. As such he edited eight volumes of the *Transactions*, a periodical not his own but which he contributed to heavily and which survived him. Still in 1868 he suggested advertising on card printed for the mail, an idea the Post Office officially adopted in 1870 and which may be said to be the forerunner of junk mail and the post card craze.

He had ideas, energy, talents and complexes; he had fixations and his own way of doing things. The result was that he had enemies, William Burns, Dr Baxter and others. Yet, he had supporters too; a group of them subscribed in 1873 and bought him a house in Forrest Hill, London.

Among them were two bishops, a moderator and ex-moderator and the foundation stone was laid by George Cruickshank, illustrator of Dickens works and friend of Rogers. That year he founded two more organisations: the English Reprint Society and in 1875 the British Genealogical Society. Of course, he was Secretary and editor of both and they published some of his own Scottish works.

When he returned from a visit to the United States in 1880 he returned to controversy in the Royal Historical Society. It was over his editing, secretaryship, increased salary and accounts. Not getting his own way, and out of sympathy among more scientific historians and gentlemen academics of scholarship, he foolishly tried to found a rival society just as he had done 20 years before with the Wallace committee. In January 1881 he was forced to resign.

He was 55 and it was a predictable end to a frenetic career as writer, editor, subscription agent, etc., with a penchant for self-promotion and salaries to provide his income. His wife had died in 1880 and he retired to Edinburgh. There he continued his own Grampian Club and also wrote bitter pamphlets about his treatment.

What sort of a man was this? Was he just the motherless bairn of the strange manse of Dunino who could not get along with people? A supporter of his, in the Royal Historical Society, commented: "He is essentially a literary man; and literary men are seldom perfect accountant or good men of business". And that is a supporter letting him down gently! An opponent wrote: "He has the countenance of a bull, the voice of a lion and the hide of a rhinocerous"! That is not the conventional, douce Church of Scotland minister, is it? He was prudish, against vice but not teetotal as there is a letter where a friend regrets not being able to join him over his favourite malt. He was opinionated and stubborn and, maybe necessarily combative. Yet a poet and writer of the Wallace Monument guide in the 1930s could write "He did much to revive the soul of Scotland".

However, I have traced at least 12 libel cases he brought against detractors. There is the military Court of Inquiry by the Chaplain-General. There is the bankruptcy problem that took years to pay off. There are threatened Court of Session processes and investigations in the accounts of most of his enterprises though usually exonerated. And there are the vendettas, by others mainly, but Rogers seems to have been able to give as much as he got.

In a recent index entry to a joint Royal Historical Society and Scottish History Society publication is this: 'Rogers, Chas. Charlatan, and founder of the Royal Historical Society, d.1890'.

Is that the official line? Is that the Scottish History Society, tongue in cheek, getting back at him and the Royal Historical Society at one blow?

When he died and was buried in Edinburgh in 1890 he was 65 and one obituary says he had made his peace with his calumniators.

What had he achieved and what are we to think of him 100 years later? He was an author for 50 years, from the age of 15, and a minister for 44 years, from the age of 21. I have researched his publishing record and do not think I have a record of everything: he had written or compiled 82 books and pamphlets; he edited at least 18 more. That is a total of 100 titles before counting revised editions or multiple volumes. He founded and mainly wrote some 12 journals, newspapers and tract series. He founded and was Secretary of ten or more societies. There is no numbering the committes he started or was on. Often these activities ran simultaneously with overlapping interests and organisation.

If he had lived longer, and his difficult personality had allowed, there would have been more than that even, and wider than the usual Scottish dimension. Some of his interests he recorded in 1876:

He favoured the creation of life peers; it took Harold Wilson to do that 100 years later.

He wanted compulsory life insurance; Lloyd George had to do it 50 years later.

He thought emigration should be encouraged; ''Go West young man . . .''

He said colonies should be self-governing; so did Macmillan 100 years later.

He favoured a minimum clergy stipend; something he and his father never had.

He thought cultivators of learning should get state rewards and honours; maybe the Order of Lenin of the U.S.S.R. is not what he had in mind but there was scope for recognition and that beyond his own self-interest as he got a pension for the Ettrick Shepherd's widow.

What would he have done if, back in Scotland and a parish minister, he had been sent up as delegate to the General Assembly? What if his Scottish interests had turned him to politics and he had been an M.P.?

His most obvious achievement, against all the odds and there now for all to see, is the Wallace Monument. Certainly it would not have been there without him, the raising and organising of funds and events and the writing of all those letters. Lesser in stature or grand style are the, at least, eight other monuments he instigated in Stirling, the Borders and Edinburgh.

In 1892, after his death, a bust of Rogers was put right there in the Wallace Monument hall — beside one of William Burns, dogging him to the end.

For our purposes and interest, he was the PR man and promoter who, at only 25, made Major Henderson's ideas of Bridge of Allan an attractive proposition and a successful spa town by his book *A week at Bridge of Allan* in 1851, reprinted in 1980. And as far as I know, he never visited it for the last 25 years of his tempestuous and productive life.

Who was Charles R.O.G.E.R., or R.O.G.E.R.S., or R.O.D.G.E.R., or R.O.D.G.E.R.S.? Was he four men of activity or an incredible one?

The incredible ONE is who Charles Rogers was, that's who!

BOOK REVIEW

STIRLING THE ROYAL BURGH. Craig Mair. John Donald, Edinburgh. 255pp. ISBN 0 085976 272 6. £13.95.

This book is of particular interest to the *Forth Naturalist and Historian* whose objectives are to help further interest in the natural and social history and environment of Stirling and central Scotland. It is, as the author says in his preface, a straightforward history for general reading, and an excellent broad picture he certainly has achieved, with Stirling put into the context of Scottish history, and presented in an attractive format for reading, and for appreciating the numerous and pertinent illustrations.

''There can be few Scottish burghs with a history to rival that of Stirling'' says the colourful bookjacket — featuring castle, auld brig and Darnley House in festive attire. Publisher and author are to be congratulated for this very readable, attractive, absorbingly interesting work which succeeds in putting this university and tourist town — set in scenic central Scotland, gateway to the Highlands — into historically significant perspective. Its key position in Scottish history and heritage, and its many associated influential and famous people — kings and queens, patriots, soldiers, scientists, politicians, merchants, churchmen, martyrs — are well featured in the fourteen chapters. These take us from Life before the Burgh of 1120; through Wallace and Bruce 1290-1370; Castle, Mediaeval town, and Mary Queen of Scots and James VI to 1603; Cromwell and the Union; through The Jacobites; and then Times of agricultural and industrial change c1750 to 1830; Into the Victorian era; the Turn of the century; through The wars to 1950; and finally Into the future.

The latter touches on the ''demolition 1950s'', years when the top of the town was ''a scene of gaping houses and rubble — 250 tons carried away every working day for over seven years''; and how the burgh architect with Historic Buildings Council and others saved or restored some of the notable buildings described in Lindsay and Court's timely and influential booklet of 1948 *Old Stirling*. Stirling the author suggests was gratefully spared the worst of that 1960s period of dreadful building in Britain; its Thistle Centre could have been **much** worse and it has preserved the unique bastion and battle dungeon, and displays some flavour of the old burgh's crafts and merchants in the concourse frieze and banners.

Briefly touching on the impact of the coming of the University the author closes the main text in thinking "the future does not look so bad. Stirling still has the feeling of a small town in a beautiful setting . . . is an enjoyable place in which to live and work . . . if the ghosts of Stirling are watching, it is we hope with a smile of approval".

Finally the book rounds off with a useful five pages of further reading notes under headings — general; castle and local battles; burgh history; buildings; neighbouring communities; for younger readers (important for education today); and for the more serious — a few notes on documentary sources. For the general reader one might suggest a start in further reading with the complementary burgh histories of Lannon and McNaughton — the *Making of Modern Stirling* and *A History of Old Stirling*, also McCutcheon's *Stirling Observer 150 years on* and McKean's *Stirling and the Trossachs* — a few of Lannon are still purchasable, the others through libraries or second hand, as would be Nimmo's *History of Stirlingshire*. Nimmo as the first and basic history of the larger area has the University's 1974 survey *The Stirling Region* nearer us in time. These all, as the author says, have greater details in some subjects e.g. the early days, the buildings, sport, transport, photos.

Our *Forth Naturalist and Historian's* 13 volumes to date have some 150 papers on many naturalist and historial subjects over the last 14 years. I might just quote a few of these — Sources of history by McKichen vol. 2 1977; Newspapers as a source of local history, vol. 3; the Labour movement by Young vol. 4; Nimmo first historian of Stirling, and the Poor Law and Stirling, vol. 5; Attitudes of Stirling clergy, and Robert Kidston, vol. 8; Fisher Row — Stirling in late 17C by John Harrison, vol. 9; and his Hearth Tax and population of Stirling in 1691 in vol. 10, which also included Jayne Stephenson's Oral history of Stirling women; David Bruce, and Stirling 1734, in vol. 11; and Early gravestones in Holy Rude in this vol. 13. Additionally these volumes have authoritative annual surveys of climate and weather, and of bird observations.

One might note that a motivating factor in our establishing the *Forth Naturalist and Historian* in the mid-1970s was to carry on the traditions of that major source of Stirling information the *Transactions of the Stirling Field and Archaeological Society* 1878-1939 which have a wealth of local studies by notable contributors. These all add to the valuable background surveys by the three *Statistical Accounts of Scotland* of the 1790s, 1830s and post World War II series.

Stirling the Royal Burgh is then an excellent introduction to its history, a broad picture, well written and produced. Perhaps Craig Mair in time might favour us with more in like manner on Stirling into the year 2000!

L. Corbett

BOOK REVIEW

PEOPLE AND SOCIETY IN SCOTLAND 1830-1914. W. Hamish Fraser and R. J. Morris, editors. A Social History of Modern Scotland volume 2 of three volumes. The Economic and Social History Society of Scotland and John Donald. 1990. 363pp. ppbk. ISBN 0 85976 2114. £12.50.

This is a collection of learned articles tackling a wide range of social, political, and economic issues in the Scotland of 1830 to 1914. Most of the contributors are 'heavyweight' academic historians working in Scottish universities.

In his short introductory piece called 'The Making of a Nation Within a Nation', R. J. Morris gives a punchy and promising distillation of the subject-matter and the shape of things to come. Chapter One is 'The People' by M. Anderson and D. J. Morse, a lengthy but very welcome econometric mapping-out of the wider framework for the more specific articles which follow. Thus, Chapter Two is a rigorous study of 'The Rural Experience' by R. H. Campbell and T. M. Devine, and Chapter Three finds the busy R. J. Morris turning an equally sharp spotlight on 'Urbanisation and Scotland'. The titles of the other chapters are, in order of appearance:– The Dominant Classes; The Political and Workplace Culture of the Scottish Working Class; The Occupied Male Labour Force; Women's Spheres; Developments in Leisure; Poverty, Health, and Welfare; An Exploration Into Scottish Education; Religion, Class, and Church Growth; and Community And Culture.

The articles are all rich in scholarly apparatus and flavour, with clear and precise references given after each chapter. The book has over 60 attractive photographs, and a very good general index. Despite the careful demarcation of major themes, a good deal of subject-matter overlap inevitably occurs, and some bits of some chapters do tend to read like slightly different versions of the same reality. This is often necessary and desirable, though, and for this reason some readers will be especially glad of the excellent index.

Time and again in the book, some local experiences of Stirling and the surrounding area are satisfyingly clicked into the wider world. Stirling's innovations in public health, for instance, along with the notorious reluctance to levy and to pay burgh rates, and the blatant apartheid and class-conflicts within Stirling Country Cricket Club, are all pointed-up sharply when set against similar events in other places. It's all so enjoyable melodic. I remember hearing Finlay McKichan delivering, as a guest speaker at Stirling University in 1976, what was in essence a 'Stirling stinks' hypothesis, convincingly based on evidence of slums and squalour at the old top of the town. In the opening chapter of the book under review here, the same kind of formidable spadework is employed on the same topic to reveal that Stirling, along with Montrose, had in fact the highest death-rates in the whole of Scotland. So much for the popular myth that the big cities were the main hotbeds of early death from dirt and disease. Having long suspected that Stirling has smudged the air with a lethal pong, I'm now grateful for this extra proof.

Another Stirling feature is a reprint of an advert in a *Stirling Observer* of 1858. Pungent with original testimony, it announces the sale of property at Stirling Castle and also refers to the sale of a pew in the East Church complete with chronic dose of anxiety about the expected status of buyers ane sellers. Elsewhere in the book we are told of the strict Sunday-schools at the Cowane Church Centre and the South Church as revealed by the Stirling Women's Oral History Archive located in the Smith Museum.

Among the clamour of topics ringing loud and clear from this volume, there are a few eerie silences. The prevalence and role of freemasonry is neglected, for instance. For an issue now so high on the public agenda, some attempt to make sense of it would have been solidly relevant. Also, the Victorian period saw the grand-scale disabling and segregation of so many people with physical, sensory, and mental impairments. M. A. Crowther, in the chapter 'Poverty, Health, and Welfare' does offer some coverage of patterns of service-provision and 'care' for 'the poor', 'lunatics', 'the insane' and the likes, and this is fine as far as it goes. Perhaps future works could expand and develop the opportunities for even deeper and more sensitive understandings of this sector. In their chapter about 'The Dominant Classes', N. Morgan and R. H. Trainor come closer to a fertile concept of paupers as the oppressed playthings of the better-off. Again, this is useful, but it deserves to be developed into a full-blown exploration of the birth of so many disabling barriers, including physical structures and exploitive professionalism, which cropped up in this period and percolated into conventional wisdom. After all, Eleanor Gordon gets a whole chapter in the book to wax lyrical about the plight of women, so where are the voices of the other oppressed groups?

No-one should be alarmed or surprised if the dominant narrative style in these pages doesn't always fly like a dove from the hands. It's a Klondike of high-powered historical works, and the multiple nuggets are there for the taking. There should be no hestitation in strongly recommending this book to the serious student.

Tom Lannon

THE ROYAL HUNT OF A LION
CHARLES DICKENS AT BRIDGE OF ALLAN

David Angus

Two inscriptions decorated the facade of the Royal Hotel in Bridge of Allan till 1989 (see p 117).

One states (erroneously) that Robert Louis Stevenson stayed there in April and May 1867. In fact the 16-year-old Stevenson spent these months with his parents at Darnley House, further along Henderson Street to the east, but for some reason did not wish to publicise the fact. It was another Mr Stevenson who stayed at the Royal at that time. R.L.S. did stay at the Royal Hotel as a boy, again with his parents, April 9th-12th, **1862**.

The other inscription, curiously, also relates to 1867, but this one tells the plain truth. Charles Dickens, then at the height of his fame and fortune, did stay at the Royal from Tuesday, February 19th until Thursday, February 21st. A cameo of the great man's bearded head, in profile, is set above this inscription. The Dickens plaque was put up in June 1938 at the instance of the Glasgow Dickens Society and the Edinburgh branch of the Dickens Fellowship, who had already met on February 19th that same year to celebrate the 71st anniversary of the novelist's coming to Bridge of Allan.

What a pity the times of the two visits — Stevenson's and Dickens' — did not coincide! The nearest Stevenson ever came to Dickens (so far as we know) was a temporary quarrel 21 years later with Dickens' son and namesake, R.L.S. having evidently criticised the older novelist for an alleged inability to create 'a gentleman' among his characters.

So — Dickens and Stevenson seem to have missed each other by a couple of months, and here as elsewhere a miss was as good as a mile. The lion escaped. Or — did he? No so cleanly, I would guess. What brought Dickens to Bridge of Allan in the first place? It was what took him to many parts of Great Britain and the U S A — his public readings from his own works.

Early in 1867 Dickens was in the midst of the third of four reading-tours (financially rewarding, physically over-taxing) which he undertook in this country. He had just given a performance in Glasgow (a sell-out to a wildly enthusiastic audience, like all the others) and had now a few days to wait before giving another. Someone (probably his tour-manager, friend and travelling-companion, George Dolby) must have suggested a brief break away from the grinding and hectic tour-routine. Even in 1867 (and he had a tour and a half in Britain and a complete tour in America still to go) Dickens' life was a constant struggle against ill-health, aggravated by tour conditions.

Writing to his daughter from Glasgow, two days before the Bridge of Allan break began, he describes "a curious feeling of soreness all round the body, which I suppose to arise from the great exertion of voice (in the readings)". He had in fact been in a worse state in Glasgow than this suggests, and had lost a good deal of blood.

Dickens arrived (no doubt by train) with his little entourage at Bridge of Allan at mid-day on the Tuesday. With him were three attendants, including his excellent valet, Scott, and of course George Dolby, his tall, bluff, stammering tour-manager who (according to Dickens) seemed to wish to knock down any stranger who addressed his charge anywhere.

Writing to his beloved sister-in-law Georgina Hogarth from the Royal Hotel, late on the 19th, Dickens admitted that after his bout of sickness in Glasgow he had found that to begin the reading of the evening of the 18th had required "a little more exertion" than usual, and then he had spent a sleepless night. But the balmy air of Bridge of Allan (he seems to have eschewed the waters) had had its customary beneficent effect. By the evening of the 19th he was, he assured Miss Hogarth, "in good force and spirits . . . I may say in the best force".

A few days before, at a Liverpool hotel, Dickens had been almost asphyxiated by paint fumes. The gentle breezes of the spa, then, were particularly welcome and wholesome in their effect. He concludes the letter to his sister-in-law thus:– "The quiet of this little place is sure to do me good. The little inn in which we are established seems a capital house of the best country sort". His spirit felt soothed as well as his shattered body.

Dickens appears to have strolled about Bridge of Allan or rested up at the Royal on the afternoon and evening of the Tuesday. He did not, unfortunately, sleep that night, or the next, since insomnia and the waking nightmares of a hyperactive imagination and too-vivid memory plagued him everywhere. (See his essay 'Lying Awake'). Stevenson, on the other hand, had found Bridge of Allan a marvellous cure for his night fears, and later wrote a poem in praise of it for that. Nevertheless, despite insomnia, Dickens did not let the grass grow under his feet next day. The nearest place of interest, in his eyes, was Stirling, two miles away. He determined to visit it.

So next morning he and the protective Dolby set out, in true Victorian fashion, to see the Royal Burgh on foot. The great man's appearance, of course, was familiar to many. Word had by now got about the village of his august presence, and so we may be sure that as the two men strolled along Henderson Street, heading east towards Stirling, nudges, stares and murmured remarks greeted their progress at every step.

Things were quieter out on the Airthrey Road, but here there was much to take their attention. The majestic profile of Stirling Castle on its rock loomed to their right over the then-uncluttered carse, and directly ahead, on the wooded Abbey Craig, the mighty column of the Wallace Monument stood three-parts built. (It opened in 1870, the year of Dickens' death.).

At Causewayhead village the two turned south along (virtually) the line of the ancient man-made mound that ran towards Stirling Bridge. They marched along a still almost rural road, upon ground once drenched with the blood of Wallace's victory of 1297.

Whether they crossed the Forth by the medieval Auld Brig or by Robert Stevenson's then-modern Stirling Bridge is a moot point. And how much Dickens (or Dolby) knew of the history of this place or sensed of the warring ghosts about them is another. But as the novelist later described the walk as 'interesting', one guesses a good deal.

Charles Dickens had indeed passed this way as early as 1841, when he was 29, on his way to an adventurous, uncomfortable and even hazardous tour of the Highlands in execrable weather. (He would not, however, have seen the Royal Hotel then, for that went up two years later).

In Stirling that February day the pair evidently refreshed themselves — I suspect at the Golden Lion in King Street. Here, 80 years earlier, another literary lion, the 28-year-old Robert Burns (who stayed there when it was still new, still 'Wingate's') had met some of the literati of the burgh, including Dr David Doig, Rector of the High School, Christopher Bell of the English School in Baxter's Wynd (Baker Street), and Lieutenant Gabriel Forrester of the Castle garrison. Indeed he had supped with them, with much song and mirth.

In the Golden Lion (or wherever) Dickens and Dolby met with the 1867 counterparts of Doig, Bell and Forrester — men whom the novelist ironically referred to as the 'lions of Stirling'. I suspect they must have heard of Dickens' approach from some scout and lain in wait for him. Alas, he does not mention their names or the subjects of their talk, but (in a letter to his daughter written on his return to Glasgow) he did remark that he "(strange to relate) was not bored by them".

As he says earlier in the same letter, he was, after the rest at Bridge of Allan, "in renewed force", having been "in excellent air all day" since his arrival. Dickens was of a buoyant and resilient disposition, and so suffered 'the lions' at Stirling, it seems, very gladly. Indeed (he goes on) "they (the lions) left me so fresh that I knocked at the gate of the prison" (it still stands in St. John Street restored as a Stirling Heritage feature, and was at that time the civil prison of Stirling), "presented myself to the governor, and took Dolby over the jail, to his unspeakable interest. We then walked back to our excellent country inn".

A prison might seem an odd place to inspect. But Dickens had learned about prisons all too intimately as a child when his improvident father

John Dickens (the original of Micawber) had languished in the Marshalsea for debt. Dickens, that great social reformer and student of human nature, loved to move (sometimes with police protection) among the lower criminal classes and 'the unfortunates' to hear their stories, study their characters and examine the human condition at the level termed by Gorki 'the lower depths'. Prisons drew him as a magnet draws filings. And he had never been in a Scottish gaol.

We are indebted to George Dolby for an account of the visit. This is taken from his memoir 'Charles Dickens as I remember him', published in 1885:

''At the inhospitable-looking door a warder answered our knock, and Mr Dickens sent in his card to the governor, who with true politeness came to the gate to receive us. Mr Dickens explained that, though he had seen much of gaols, he had never been inside a Scottish gaol. There was no difficulty whatever about the matter, and the governor, with a couple of warders, conducted us personally through the establishment, opening all the cell doors and allowing us to converse with their tenants.

Here and there Mr Dickens said kind and comforting words to the prisoners, which seemed to be a relief to them in their miserable position.

We were about to enter one cell to say a few words to a boy confined in it, but finding him reading a Bible with a gentleman in clerical attire, we retired, thinking that perhaps the boy was receiving spiritual consolation from the chaplain. When the door was locked, I observed an amused expression on the Govenor's face, and inquired of him the nature of the boy's offence.

He was a London boy, who had been imported into Scotland by a gang of native burglars — London boys being more expert in the 'trade' than Scottish lads. The boy had not much hard labour in the exercise of his calling, for, like Oliver Twist, he was passed through a window to make an inspection of the interior of the house, and open a door, either back or front, to enable the burglars to enter without interference. Unluckily for this particular boy, he did not understand the construction of Scotch houses, and during his first job got 'lagged', whilst his friends contrived to escape.

It was not the boy, though, that the kind-hearted governor was laughing (at), but at Mr Dickens and myself, and at our respectful demeanour to the boy's spiritual adviser, who was none other than a celebrated bank forger — a lithographer by trade — who had successfully forged banknotes to a large amount, and had gone off to America with the spoil. In New York he had represented himself as a clergyman, and had been appointed with a large stipend to one of the leading churches in America, where he did duty for some time.

Supposing that he and his crime had been forgotten, he returned to Glasgow to arrange some private affairs, and, in an unfortunate moment (for him), was recognised, arrested, and condemned to penal servitude''.

The next stage of their visit must have struck a particular chord in Dickens' breast. Dolby proceeds:

''The criminal side of the gaol being disposed of, we were conducted to the debtors' side, and here incarceration had quite another aspect. Here were some fifteen or twenty persons in a large room, with a comfortable blazing fire. Some were playing draughts and dominoes, others reading newspapers or books, and all seemed to enjoy themselves, and regard us as intruders in their happiness''.

''The Marshalsea'', Dickens must have thought, ''was never like this''.

''One of the debtors'' (Dolby goes on) ''recognized Mr Dickens, who was very soon surrounded by this queer company. Some pointed out to him the folly and iniquity of confining them in prison until their debts were paid; but most of them expressed themselves highly pleased with their lot, and declared that so long as their creditors chose to pay for their maintenance, they were quite content to stay where they were; for, except that they were deprived of the privilege of smoking, they were far happier, had better beds on which to sleep, and could get better food at a cheaper rate (out of their allowance) than many of them were in the habit of getting outside.

The regret of our friends at parting with us appeared to be great, one of them pleasantly observing, 'When I saw you gentlemen come in I was in hopes we were going to have you as fellow-lodgers for a time at the 'Stirling Castle Hotel' '.

Our trip to the Bridge of Allan'' (adds Dolby) ''was productive of the greatest benefit to Mr Dickens' health, and he went back to his work on the platform with the old **verve**''.

Incidentally Charles Dickens Jr. also visited Stirling, in November 1891 — three years after the quarrel with Stevenson — and went one better than his father by giving readings from the latter's works in the Town Hall; from *David Copperfield* and the *Pickwick Papers*. But he was not the man his father had been. A heavy cold affected his performance, the audience was sparse, and the *Stirling Journal's* reporter (from whom I learn all this) seems to have left at the interval!

To return to Dickens Sr. The news of the great man's charming accessibility in Stirling must soon have spread like wildfire through Bridge of Allan. The novelist, pleasantly tired out by his excursion, may well have guessed at this and its likely effect that evening. Or perhaps the anxious Dolby did. But I leave the rest of this little story to the anonymous satirist who, a few days later, recounted the events (or non-events) of that Wednesday evening, in the *Stirling Journal* in the section devoted to Bridge of Allan news. He has a pleasantly sardonic style!

"The guidnuncs (gossips) of our village were in a pretty *qui vive* (state of excitement) one day this week. It had got around that a distinguished living author was staying at one of our hotels, and the desire to see him, perchance to be kicked by him, after a famous royal example, was too much for the little wits of our great folk.

He was stared at from the pavements, curiously watched from curtained windows, and broadly spoken about ere the passer-by had well seen his back. The affair, however, reached the height of the ridiculous when a few of the 'wiser sort', who knew a thing or two, as well as the value of a boar (=lion?), planned to catch the gentleman in the smoking-room.

It was well devised. The hour and the man were both anticipated with some impatience. Cigars of the choicest brand were inclosed in cases of the rarest material, and most elegant as well as most fanciful form. Of other tobaccos and scents and starch we may not tell all we know; nor may we mention the studied ease which each assumed as, drawing his glass near him, he poised himself on his chair, with just half an eye on the door, lest another should catch a first glimpse of the great man.

Several who dropped in quite 'promiscuous-like' were voted bores. Conversation sadly flagged, local gossip was too insipid, and no-one ventured to introduce anything knowing how quickly he might be put down. It was amusing to witness the seeming indifference but real anxiety of our local toadies. Every one had ears behind his back that night, and the buzz of pretended conversation which, every now and then was got up to drown 'Here he comes' would, had it reached his ears, have tickled the great man, and made some of them immortal.

But the best-laid schemes of men and mice — you know the rest. Our tuft-hunters were disappointed, and, after enjoying but poorly their good tipple, they betook themselves homeward, conscious of having made fools of themselves, but sworn to secrecy.

The idea was indeed boorish. The illustrious C.D. to be bored in the smoking-room of his hotel!"

It was not, come to think of it, particularly well-devised either. The last thing Dickens wished at this time was a room thick with tobacco-smoke. In the smokeless zone of the debtors' prison he had lingered.

Next day Mr Dickens, blissfully unaware of the smoking-room farce of the night before (but perhaps suspecting it for all that) took train again to Glasgow to give yet another reading of his magazine story 'Dr Marigold's Prescriptions'. (It is a sentimental, long-forgotten piece about a quack doctor who adopts a deaf-and-dumb girl but then stands aside nobly to let her marry a deaf-and-dumb admirer. And so Charles Dickens passed out of Bridge of Allan's ken except as a name in the newspapers, and on the title-pages of his novels.

There is a hidden irony in the satirist's account of that evening without Dickens — for, after all, he too must have been one of that tense company, and sat as keyed-up and uncertain as any of them as the empty hours passed. But a couple of days later he had evidently distanced himself enough to see the ridiculous side of it — at least as that applied to others! And if the truth be told, the squib he wrote then is not absolutely unworthy of the pen of Dickens himself — or of that 'sedulous ape', the young Robert Louis Stevenson.

It is possible the latter was at Bridge of Allan — and the Royal Hotel — after all, on **another** anonymous visit? That **he** was the mischievous "chiel . . . takin notes" among the tuft-hunters that awkward winter's evening? And that he — even he — was "sworn to secrecy" out of shame for his part in the whole ridiculous business?

We shall never know.

The Dickens and Stevenson plaques at the Royal Hotel Bridge of Allan.
D. Angus

The Old Prison, Stirling – southern frontage as seen from the west 1990

D. Angus

Authors' Addresses

Allan, J. Malcolm, 28 Kenilworth Road, Bridge of Allan
Angus, David, 122 Henderson Street, Bridge of Allan
Bain, Andrew, 22 Clarendon Road, Linlithgow
Corbett, Lindsay, 30 Dunmar Drive, Alloa
Duck, Dr R. W., Purdie Building, Dept. of Geography, University of St. Andrews
Harrison, John G., 14a Abercromby Place, Stirling
Harrison, S.J., Environmental Science, University of Stirling
Henty, C.J. University of Stirling
Lannon, Tom, 40c Cow Wynd, Falkirk
Mitchell, John, 22 Muirpark Way, Drymen
Murphy, D., 18 Forth Crescent, Stirling
Stroud, David, Ornithology Branch, Nature Conservancy Council, Peterborough – for the Moorland Birds paper